FOR THE LOVE OF DOLLS

The Legendary Collection of Mildred Seeley

FOREWORD BY FLORENCE THERIAULT

GOLD HORSE PUBLISHING

To order additional copies contact:
Dollmasters, PO Box 2319, Annapolis, MD 21401
Tel. 800-966-3655   Fax 410-571-9605
www.dollmasters.com

Quotations from books by Mildred Seeley are used with permission of Jones Publishing.

Design: Deborah VanDereedt
Photography: Chris Brady & Colby Kuschatka

$49
ISBN: 1-931503-06-0
Printed in Hong Kong

Foreword

It's been four months since I learned that Mildred Seeley has left this earthly vale. "Earthly vale". How Millie would have laughed at that phrase. Those who were fortunate enough to know her can almost hear her signature bubbly laughter filling the room at the thought of such a fancy phrase to describe her life.

During those four months I've read many stories of praise about Millie, as she was known to all who were graced to have her acquaintance. Each of these stories praises her as a woman of generosity – welcoming, inclusive and sharing. And all of this is true. Yet as I read these stories I kept feeling something was missing. She was certainly all of those things, but there was something more. I finally settled upon one word that best sums the Millie that I knew and admired. Spunky. The woman was spunky.

That's an old-fashioned word, but Millie was an old-fashioned kind of lady. She believed in hard work, fair is fair, and loyalty. She was generous almost to a fault, but she didn't suffer fools gladly. And if you spent time around her sooner or later you found out that she spoke her mind, and sometimes you were at the hard end of that speaking. Spunky she was, but spunky tempered with good grace, intelligence and the ability to laugh at herself. That was the Millie I knew and remember with a special fondness.

It takes such spunkiness to build a world-class collection. The courage to choose and the courage to pursue. In her autobiography, *For the Love of Dolls and Roses*, Millie said she spent her entire life savings to buy the Marque doll that she had spent years pursuing. At auctions she went up against other collectors and dealers with fearless certainty. Her tenacity in tracking down a doll was boundless, although softened by the special joy she felt when that doll came to live at her home.

It is a lesson for today's collectors that Millie did not come from wealth. She did, in fact, come to adulthood during the Depression Years of the 1930's, and her early childhood was not an easy one in terms of financial wealth. But from her rural New York state roots she gathered a reverence for old things. Coupling this reverence with good common sense, she managed to parlay her collection into one of the finest of the world. How was this possible? It was by a constant evaluation of her dolls. A particular mantra of her seminars was the advice to new collectors to "upgrade, upgrade, upgrade", and for those who wonder how a person of ordinary means can build such a world-class collection that is her simple instruction. Each time that Millie acquired a second example of a doll she compared it to the others in her collection and kept the best.

Although I had known that Millie collected according to that rule, I never realized its impact until I came to prepare this book. Here was the result. It was simple but its impact was powerful and vivid. The collection of Mildred Seeley was honed to have become the best of the best. She judged her dolls with the eye of an artist, guarding for herself those with the most beautiful sculpting and finest clarity of bisque and painting. You will find that to be evident with the dolls in this book.

Millie loved doll auctions. For her they combined the joy of seeing hundreds of dolls, choosing a special favorite (or two or three), entering the fray to compete for that doll, and, of course, winning. As pleasurable, too, was the fun of greeting old friends, meeting new ones, laughing, talking, learning. Millie would have loved being at her own auction.

In writing this, I realize with a jolting awareness that when I first met Millie she was the age that I am today. That was twenty years ago. And then I remember all that Millie accomplished during that last twenty years of her life – books, seminars, travel, garden, collecting, building a new home – in short, the fulsome life of a vigorous person. Toward the end, when her body failed her ambition, she still continued to dream and plan and inspire others.

It was Mildred Seeley's desire that her collection be returned to the collecting world. Such pleasure had been hers in being a "keeper of the dolls" that she wished others to also have that opportunity. In such a spirit this book has been written.

Florence Theriault
April, 2002

DEDICATION: Several years ago Millie hinted that I might be preparing a commemorative catalog of her dolls some day. At that time, she asked me to dedicate the book to her late husband, Vern Seeley, and her children, Colleen and Jay. She loved her dolls. She loved her family far more.

From *For the Love of Dolls and Roses* by Mildred Seeley.
Photo used with the permission of Jones Publishing.

1. A Gorgeous French Bisque Bebe E.J. by Jumeau

25" (63 cm). Pressed bisque socket head, blue glass paperweight inset eyes, dark eyeliner encircles the eyecut, painted lashes, mauve blushed eyeshadow, widely arched brushstroked and feathered brows, accented eye corners, shaded nostrils, closed mouth with accented lips, dimpled chin and lip corners, separated applied and pierced ears, blonde mohair wig over cork pate, French composition and wooden fully jointed body with straight wrists. CONDITION: generally excellent, original body finish. MARKS: Depose E. 12 J. (and artist checkmarks on head). COMMENTS: Emile Jumeau, his first registered model bebe, circa 1885, made for one or two years only. VALUE POINTS: rare large size 12 of the gorgeous bebe has superb bisque, painting and eyes, mohair wig, original body, antique costume comprising cutwork dress, undergarments, burgundy velvet coat and cap, leather shoes with burgundy silk rosettes signed "Paris Depose 12" with star symbol. $7500/9500

2. French Bisque Bebe Jumeau as Marquis

22" (56 cm). Bisque socket head, dark blue glass paperweight inset eyes, dark eyeliner encircles the eyecut, lushly painted lashes, brushstroked and feathered brows, accented nostrils and eye corners, closed mouth with defined space between the shaded and outlined lips, pierced ears, brunette mohair wig arranged as periwig, French composition and wooden fully-jointed body. CONDITION: generally excellent. MARKS: Depose Tete Jumeau SGDG 10 (and artist checkmarks, on head) Jumeau Medaille d'Or Paris (body). COMMENTS: Emile Jumeau, circa 1888. VALUE POINTS: fine quality of bisque, painting, original body and body finish, unusual periwig and antique couturier-made Marquis costume of cherry-red velvet with metallic edging, lace cuffs and jabot, silk knee-length pants. The doll was featured in *The Jumeau Book* by Theimer and Theriault. $4500/5500

3. The Beautiful French Bisque Portrait Poupee by Pierre-Francois Jumeau

21" (53 cm). Pressed bisque swivel head on kid-edged bisque shoulderplate, almond shaped small blue glass enamel inset eyes with spiral threading, dark eyeliner encircles the eyecuts, painted lashes, lightly feathered brows, mauve blushed eyeshadow, separately modelled and pierced ears, blonde mohair wig over cork pate, French kid gusset-jointed fashion body with shapely waist and derriere, gusset-jointed hips and knees, separated toes, bisque forearms with detailed sculpting of fingers, antique (frail) green-bronze silk gown, green velvet bonnet, undergarments, brown leather boots, and wonderful antique silk parasol. CONDITION: generally excellent, small edge-roughness at back edge of shoulderplate, left baby finger restored, body is sturdy but a bit discolored. COMMENTS: Pierre-Francois Jumeau, circa 1870. VALUE POINTS: an exceptionally beautiful example of the early portrait model. In her book *Lady Dolls*, Mildred Seeley described "the head itself is beautiful, a work of art. It is very translucent and the face has a glow". $3500/4500

4. An Extraordinary Pair of French Bisque Dolls in Brittany Wedding Costumes

24" and 25" (61 and 63 cm). Each doll has a bisque shoulderhead with plumply modelled facial features, cobalt blue glass inset eyes, dark eyeliner, painted lashes, arched feathered brows, accented nostrils and eye corners, closed mouth with accented lips, ears pierced into head, well detailed blushing, French pink kid fashion body with gusset jointed elbows, stitched and separated fingers, shapely plump bodies with one piece shaped legs. CONDITION: generally excellent. MARKS: F. 8. G. (boy). COMMENTS: Gaultier, circa 1869, according to Seeley's book *Doll Costuming*, the dolls were once accompanied by a paper label reading "Brittany Wedding, 1869". VALUE POINTS: exceptional size of the early poupees wearing their original well-preserved folklore costumes from the Finistiere region of Brittany, the man with black jacket, sleeveless vest ("chupen"), flared pants ("bragou braz") with tasseled yarn ties at the knees, fitted leggings, black cap, all trimmed with elaborate embroidery; the woman with fitted bodice under black sleevesless vest, red wooden skirt, coiffe, undergarments. The pair of dolls graced the front entrance hall of the Seeley home for more than two decades. $8000/12,000

5. French Bisque Poupee in Original Folklore Costume of Normandy

13" (33 cm). Bisque swivel head on kid-edged bisque shoulderplate, pale blue glass enamel inset eyes, painted lashes and feathered brows, accented nostrils and eye corners, closed mouth with accented lips, pierced ears, blonde mohair wig over cork pate, French fashion body with muslin torso and legs, kid arms with gusset-jointed elbows, stitched and separated fingers. CONDITION: generally excellent. MARKS: 0 (head and shoulderplate). COMMENTS: Gaultier, circa 1875. VALUE POINTS: the fashion lady is in pristine unplayed with condition, wearing costume of the Normandy region of France including elaborate coiffe, paisley shawl, jewelry. $3000/3500

“ **I always prefer to collect dolls in original costumes. I believe in preserving them as a bit of history, an artifact.** ”

For the Love of Dolls and Roses,
Autobiography of Mildred Seeley

6. Early French Bisque Poupee
in Original Folklore Costume of Brittany

14" (35 cm). Pale bisque swivel head on kid-edged bisque shoulderplate, pale blue glass inset eyes, painted lashes, delicately feathered brows, accented nostrils and eye corners, closed mouth with accented lips, pierced ears, blonde mohair wig over cork pate, French fashion body with shapely muslin torso and legs, kid arms with gusset-jointed elbows, stitched and separated fingers. CONDITION: generally excellent. MARKS: 1. COMMENTS: maker unknown, circa 1865. VALUE POINTS: the beautiful early model poupee wears a wonderfully preserved original folklore costume from Brittany including elaborate lace coiffe and black velvet "parure de cou". $3500/4500

7. Extremely Rare French Bisque Doll by Albert Marque with Original Margaine-Lacroix Costume

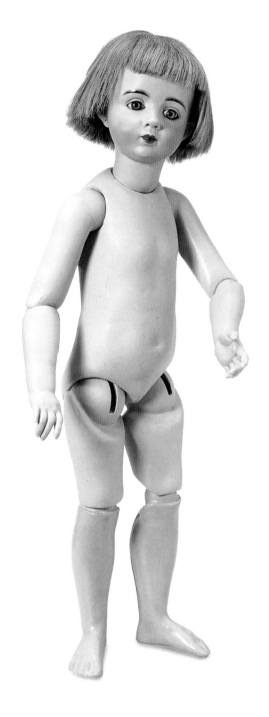

22" (56 cm). Bisque socket head portraying an older wistful-faced child with prominent definition of facial planes and high domed forehead achieved by use of a unique four-part mold, blue glass paperweight inset eyes, painted curly lashes, darker lower lashes, brushstroked and feathered brows, accented eye corners, distinctively shaped nose with rounded tip, accented eye corners and nostrils, closed mouth with shaded and accented lips, distinctively shaped ears, pierced ear holes, original red mohair wig in bobbed cut, unique body with elongated tapered shape torso, wide hips, undefined waist, elongated composition upper arms, bisque lower arms with attached bisque ball-joints at the elbows, separately sculpted fingers, wide upper thighs, elongated lower legs with shapely calves, slender ankles, elongated feet. The doll wears original costume from the studio of Parisian couturier Margaine-Lacroix, comprising grey twill suspendered knickers, silk shirt front, green velvet jacket, leather leggings, signed Alart leather shoes, and floppy straw cap with applied berries. The jacket has the original silk label of Margaine-Lacroix. CONDITION: generally excellent. MARKS: A. Marque (incised on head) 19 (red pencil script on head) Margaine-Lacroix, 19 Boulevard Haussman, Paris (cloth label). COMMENTS: France, circa 1916, the portrait doll was commissioned from and sculpted by the esteemed French artist, Albert Marque, and presented in the Parisian boutique of Margaine-Lacroix in a limited series of 100 dolls, each numbered in order of its production. The dolls were costumed by the studio to represent French regions or royalty. The body, uniquely sculpted for the Marque doll head, was designed by French artist Aristodema Botta. VALUE POINTS: an exceptionally rare doll, #19 of the limited series, has outstanding bisque and painting, original costume representing "berger" with boutique label.

This Marque doll was considered by Mildred Seeley to be the keystone of her collection and was in her possession for more than thirty years. The provenance of this Marque is known. It had been acquired by antiquarian Harriet Miller in the 1930's and was then sold to the Gaynell Denson Doll Museum and, subsequently, to the Seeley Collection. $125,000/150,000

**8. French Bisque Poupee
by Pierre-Francois Jumeau in Original Costume**

17" (43 cm). Pale bisque swivel head on kid-edged bisque shoulderplate, cobalt blue glass enamel inset eyes, painted lashes, feathered brows, accented nostrils and eye corners, closed mouth with accented lips, pierced ears, blonde mohair wig over cork pate, French kid body with gusset jointed hips and knees, shapely torso, kid upper arms, bisque arms to above the elbows with sculpted curled fingers, dimpled elbows. CONDITION: generally excellent, left thumb broken off. COMMENTS: Pierre-Francois Jumeau, circa 1868. VALUE POINTS: very beautiful pale-complexioned poupee with bisque arms, wears original (frail) ivory silk gown, original wig with elaborate coiffure and decorative comb, Jumeau earrings. $3000/4000

). Extremely Rare French
Brown Bisque Poupee Attributed to Bru

15" (38 cm). Pressed bisque shoulderhead with
uniquely modelled portrait-like features, dark
brown complexion, elongated throat, black glass
enamel inset eyes, incised eyeliner, black
brushstroked brows, accented nostrils of
upturned nose, open mouth with shaded lips,
two rows of tiny porcelain teeth, ears pierced
into the head, black antique human hair wig over
cork pate, French kid fashion body with one
piece legs, stitch-jointing at shoulders, stitched
and separated fingers. CONDITION: generally
excellent, one lower tooth missing, body re-
colored. COMMENTS: portrait poupee attributed
to Leon Casimir Bru, circa 1868. VALUE
POINTS: an extremely rare poupee with superb
sculpting, beautiful visage, rich complexion with
enhancing lustrous patina, antique bronze silk
fashion gown, green velvet bonnet with jet bead
trim, undergarments, red leather slippers.
$4500/6500

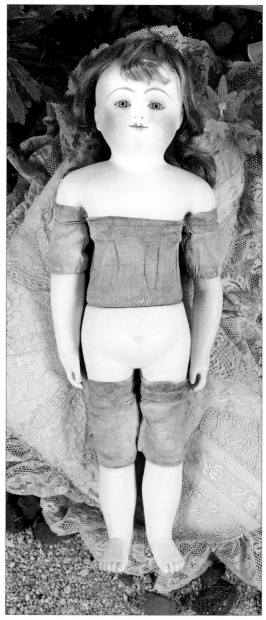

10. French Bisque Bebe Steiner in Antique Pont d'Esprit Costume

24" (61 cm). Bisque socket head, blue glass paperweight inset eyes, painted lashes with "dot" highlights, brushstroked brows with fringed highlights, accented eye corners, shaded nostrils, closed mouth with heart-shaped upper lip, shaded lips, accented nostrils, impressed dimples at chin and lip corners, pierced ears, brunette human hair over Steiner pate, French composition fully jointed body with straight wrists. CONDITION: generally excellent. MARKS: J. Steiner Bte SGDG Paris Fre A 17 (head) (original Steiner stamp on torso). COMMENTS: Jules Steiner, circa 1888. VALUE POINTS: beautiful wide-eyed child has very fine creamy bisque, artistic painting, original body and body finish, antique dress of pont d'esprit trimmed with rose silk edging and sash, undergarments, white leather ankle boots, tulle cap. $4500/5500

11. French Bisque Taufling Baby by Jules Steiner

15" (38 cm). Solid domed bisque shoulderhead with rounded facial modelling, almond shaped blue glass enamel inset eyes, painted lashes, rose blushed eyeshadow, fringed brows, accented nostrils and eye corners, closed mouth with shaded and accented lips, twill covered midriff hiding "mama" bellows crier, twill upper arms, bisque arms from above the elbows, cupped bisque hands, bisque lower torso and upper legs, twill mid-legs, bisque lower legs and feet. CONDITION: generally excellent, right baby finger broken at knuckle. COMMENTS: Jules Steiner, circa 1875, the doll was inspired by the Japanese play dolls introduced at the 1855 London Exposition, and can be considered the precursor to the French bebe of the 1880's. VALUE POINTS: rare to find this early model in such well-preserved original condition, with beautiful bisque, functioning "mama" crier. $2500/3000

**12. French Bisque Bebe,
Series A, by Jules Steiner**

22" (56 cm). Pressed bisque socket head with rounded facial modelling, blue glass paperweight inset eyes, dark eyeliner encircles the eyecut, painted lashes with "dot" highlights, rose blushed eyeshadow, brushstroked brows with fringed detail, accented eye corners, shaded nostrils, closed mouth with accented pale lips, pierced ears, dimpled chin, brunette mohair wig over Steiner cardboard pate, Steiner composition fully jointed body with straight wrists, wearing rose silk costume with lace trim, antique silk bonnet, stockings and black leather shoes with silk rosettes. CONDITION: generally excellent, roughness on upper left eye rim may be original. MARKS: Sie A 4 (incised) J. Steiner Bourguoin (red stamp) (early Steiner black caduceus stamp on torso). COMMENTS: Jules Steiner, circa 1885. VALUE POINTS: rarer model of Steiner bebe has wonderfully expressive features on plump childlike face, beautiful painting, original body with original finish. $5000/7500

13. Beautiful French Bisque Bebe by Schmitt et Fils with Boutique Label

15" (38 cm). Pressed bisque socket head with rounded facial modelling and very pale bisque, almond shaped brown glass enamel inset eyes, delicately painted lashes and brows, mauve blushed eyeshadow, accented eye corners and nostrils, closed mouth with accent line between the lips, pierced ears, lambswool wig over cork pate, French composition and wooden eight-loose-ball-jointed body with straight wrists and flat-cut derriere. CONDITION: generally excellent, small paint flake at back rim, original body finish albeit crackling on lower right arm. MARKS: Sch (in shield at back of head and derriere). COMMENTS: Schmitt et Fils, circa 1882, the doll has the original paper label of the Paris doll store Maison Bail from which it was sold. VALUE POINTS: the very beautiful bebe has choicest bisque and modelling, artistic painting, original signed body, antique costume comprising bronze silk dress with lace trim, blue leather shoes signed "Paris". A particular favorite of Mildred Seeley, the doll was featured in several of her books. $9000/13,000

14. An Outstanding French Bisque Bebe by Schmitt et Fils

28" (71 cm). Pressed bisque socket head with pear-shaped facial modelling giving a long-faced expression, large brown glass paperweight inset eyes, dark eyeliner encircles the eyecut, painted lashes, mauve blushed eyeshadow, brushstroked and multi-feathered brows, accented eye corners, shaded nostrils, closed mouth with modelled space between the shaded and accented lips, pierced ears, blonde mohair wig over cork pate, French composition and wooden eight-loose-ball-jointed body with straight wrists, separated fingers, flat-cut derriere, antique costume of aqua and ivory silk with lace trim, undergarments, extravagant bonnet, soft kid shoes. CONDITION: generally excellent. MARKS: Sch (in shield, on head) 15 (raised numbers on head) Sch (in shield, on derriere). COMMENTS: Schmitt et Fils, circa 1882. VALUE POINTS: outstanding beauty of the rare early model, her large size emphasizing the quality of sculpting and artistic facial painting, original body and body finish. $17,000/23,000

15. German Bisque Child, XI, by Kestner

16" (40 cm). Bisque socket head, brown glass sleep eyes, painted lashes, brushstroked and feathered brows, accented nostrils and eye corners, closed mouth with accent line between the pale lips, blonde mohair wig over plaster pate, early composition and wooden ball-jointed body with straight wrists, nicely costumed in white cotton dress with lace and smocking, undergarments, brown leather shoes with silver buckles. CONDITION: generally excellent. MARKS: XI. Comments: Kestner, circa 1885. VALUE POINTS: most appealing wistful-faced child whose gentle expression is complimented by delicate coloring of bisque, original wig, pate, body, body finish. $2200/2500

16. German Bisque Fashion Doll by Kestner

16" (40 cm). Solid domed bisque shoulderhead turned slightly to the right, cobalt blue glass inset eyes, painted lashes, feathered brows, accented nostrils and eye corners, closed mouth with accent line between the lips, blonde mohair wig, antique muslin stitch-jointed body with leather arms, antique lavender silk fashion gown, undergarments, leather ankle boots. CONDITION: generally excellent. COMMENTS: Kestner, circa 1885. VALUE POINTS: wide-eyed expression is enhanced by choice bisque and painting. $500/700

17. German Bisque Closed Mouth Child by Kestner
15" (38 cm). Bisque socket head, brown glass sleep eyes, painted lashes, brushstroked and feathered brows, accented nostrils and eye corners, closed mouth with accent line between the lips, brunette human hair, composition and wooden ball-jointed body. CONDITION: generally excellent. MARKS: 7 (head) IIX (incised on crown rim). COMMENTS: Kestner, circa 1890. VALUE POINTS: pretty brown-eyed closed mouth child wears antique costume, has lovely bisque, original body and body finish. $1200/1800

18. German Bisque Closed Mouth Doll by Kestner
13" (33 cm). Bisque shoulderhead, pale blue glass inset eyes, painted lashes and brows, accented nostrils and eye corners, closed mouth with center accent line, blonde mohair wig, muslin torsoed body with leather limbs, bisque forearms, nicely costumed in white gown with rose embroidery detail. CONDITION: generally excellent. MARKS: D. COMMENTS: Kestner, circa 1885. VALUE POINTS: pretty childlike features are enhanced by delicate complexion. $300/400

19. German Bisque "Country Lady" by Kestner
14" (35 cm). Bisque swivel head on kid-edged bisque shoulderplate, brown glass sleep eyes, painted lashes, arched feathered brows, accented nostrils and eye corners, closed mouth with downcast lips lending a pouty expression, blonde lambswool wig over plaster pate, kid gusset jointed body with bisque forearms. CONDITION: generally excellent. MARKS: 8. COMMENTS: Kestner, circa 1885. VALUE POINTS: exceptional quality of modelling, original body, antique costume. A particular favorite of Mildred Seeley, the doll was featured in several books including *Lady Dolls*. $800/1100

20. Rare German Bisque Character, 151, by Simon and Halbig

18" (46 cm). Bisque socket head, sculpted facial features with large painted blue/grey eyes in well-defined sockets, black upper eyeliner, one stroke brows, laughter crinkles modelled under the eyes, accented nostrils and eye corners, closed mouth in smile with accented lips, row of sculpted teeth, impressed cheek and chin dimples, blonde mohair wig, composition and wooden ball-jointed body, antique white cotton dress with Bertha collar, lace trim, undergarments, bonnet, leather shoes. CONDITION: generally excellent. MARKS: 151 S&H 7 1/2. COMMENTS: Simon and Halbig, circa 1910, from their art character series. VALUE POINTS: very rare character model with superb definition of sculpting, choice bisque and painting, original body and body finish. The doll was featured in Seeley's *German Children Dolls*. $8000/10,000

21. Very Rare German Bisque Character, 112, by Kammer and Reinhardt

22" (54 cm). Bisque socket head, painted facial features with strong characterization, large painted azure blue eyes with decorative glaze, black upper eyeliner, heavily modelled eyelids, one stroke tapered brows, accented nostrils, closed mouth with shaded and accented lips, two beaded upper teeth, blonde mohair wig, composition and wooden ball-jointed body, antique costume comprising embroidered dress, undergarments, silk ribboned bonnet, leather shoes. CONDITION: generally excellent. MARKS: K*R 112 54. COMMENTS: Kammer and Reinhardt, circa 1910, from their art reform series introduced in 1909 and made for a few years only. VALUE POINTS: very rare doll in superb large size has exceptional quality of bisque and sculpting, beautifully painted complexion and features, original body and body finish. $12,000/15,000

22. German Bisque Painted Eye Character, 526, by Kley and Hahn

19" (48 cm). Bisque socket head, painted brown eyes with glazed detail of pupils, black upper eyeliner, very short painted upper lashes, curvy feathered brows, accented nostrils and eye corners, closed mouth with center accent line, blonde mohair wig, composition and wooden ball-jointed body. CONDITION: chip and re-glue on bottom of neck socket. MARKS: K&H (in banner) 526 4 1/2. COMMENTS: Kley and Hahn, circa 1912. VALUE POINTS: pretty child with intelligent expression, wonderfully modelled expressive features, original body and body finish, antique costume. $1800/2300

23. German Bisque Character, 180, by Kestner

16" (40 cm). Bisque socket head with chubby-cheeked modelling, painted blue eyes with upper glancing pupils and white eyedots, black and red upper eyeliner with short fringed lashes, scant feathered brows, accented nostrils and eye corners, closed mouth modelled as though open, row of beaded teeth and shaded and accented lips, brunette lambswool wig over plaster pate, composition and wooden ball-jointed toddler body with shorter thighs, blue woolen boy's suit with Buster Brown collar, leather shoes, straw bonnet, undergarments. CONDITION: generally excellent. MARKS: 180. COMMENTS: Kestner, circa 1910. VALUE POINTS: rare character with very fine bisque and painting, original body and body finish. $3000/3800

24. Rare German Bisque Character, 536, by Bahr and Proschild

20" (51 cm). Bisque socket head portraying older child with deeply impressed cheek dimples, painted dark blue eyes with shaded outline, heavily modelled eyelids with black upper eyeliner and short fringed lashes, wavy feathered brows, accented nostrils and eye corners, closed mouth with very full outlined lips, blonde mohair wig, composition and wooden ball-jointed body, antique costume. CONDITION: generally excellent. MARKS: 536 8. COMMENTS: Bahr and Proschild, circa 1912. VALUE POINTS: rare model in wonderful larger size with superb detail of modelling and choicest bisque and painting, original body and body finish. $4000/5000

25. Exceptionally Rare and Beautiful French Bisque Bebe "H" by Halopeau

24" (61 cm). Pressed bisque socket head with long-cheeked modelling, dark blue glass paperweight inset eyes framed by rich black eyeliner, painted lashes with "dot" highlights, incised eyeliner, mauve blushed eyeshadow, brushstroked and multi-feathered brows, accented eye corners, shaded nostrils, closed mouth with defined space between the shaded and accented lips, dimpled chin and cheek corners, pierced ears, blonde mohair wig over cork pate, French composition and wooden fully jointed body with straight wrist, expressively posed fingers, antique white cotton/linen dress with cotton lace trim, undergarments, knit stockings, leather ankle shoes, elaborate antique bonnet. CONDITION: generally excellent. MARKS: 4 H. COMMENTS: circa 1885. The firm of Aristide Halopeau was the successor to Barrois in 1878. The firm existed and made dolls for only twelve years. (From the forthcoming *French Doll Encyclopedia* by Francois and Danielle Theimer.) VALUE POINTS: among the rarest of the French dolls, in magnificent large size, the bebe has superb bisque, sculpting and painting, original body and body finish. $40,000/60,000

25B. French Black Silk Coat and Brown Silk Bonnet

Suitable for size 10 or 11 Bebe Jumeau. The black silk satin coat has interwoven black velvet clover designs, and reversible interior of brown silk with brown plush banding. Along with brown silk bonnet with fringed edging. Very good condition. Circa 1885. $300/400

25A. French Ivory Silk Bebe Dress and Bonnet

Suitable for size 10 or 11 Bebe Jumeau. The delicate ivory silk dress with interwoven floral pattern has dropped waist, box-pleated skirt, lace Bertha collar with silk edging, lace trim at sleeves and hem. Along with ivory silk twill bonnet with wired brim, silk flow-flow ribbons and tulle, ivory silk straw streamers. Excellent condition. Circa 1885. $600/900

26. French Bisque Wooden-Bodied Poupee with Dehors Head Articulation

18" (46 cm). Pale bisque swivel head on kid-edged bisque shoulderplate, patented articulation system allows the head to tilt forward and to the sides as well as classic swivel, cobalt blue glass enamel inset eyes, dark eyeliner encircles the eyecuts, delicately painted lashes and arched brows, accented nostrils and eye corners, closed mouth with accent line between the lips, unpierced ears, auburn mohair wig over cork pate, French all wooden body with shapely adult female modelling, dowel-jointing at shoulders, elbows, hips and knees, defined cupped hands and fingers, swivel waist and upper thighs. CONDITION: generally excellent, repair to toes of right foot. COMMENTS: circa 1867, the articulation system was deposed by Alexander Dehors in 1867. VALUE POINTS: very beautiful poupee with pale complexion enhancing the cobalt blue eyes, rare Dehors system, rare wooden body with extra swivel jointing. $4000/5000

27. French Bisque Poupee with Bru Wooden Articulated Body

14" (35 cm). Bisque swivel head on kid-edged bisque shoulderplate, narrow almond shaped blue glass spiral threaded eyes, painted lashes, feathered brows, accented nostrils and eye corners, closed mouth with accented lips, pierced ears, blonde mohair wig over cork pate, all-wooden fully articulated body with dowel-jointing at shoulders, elbows, wrists, hips, knees and ankles, and ball-swivel at waist, separately sculpted fingers, kid collarette attaching shoulderplate to upper torso. CONDITION: generally excellent,

some rubs to original body finish, wood chip at left wrist. MARKS: 2. COMMENTS: the wooden articulated body was deposed by Bru in 1869. VALUE POINTS: rare wooden body in appealing petite size, antique (frail) green silk gown with train, seed pearl decoration, antique opera glasses, undergarments. $3500/4500

28. Superb French Bisque Smiling Poupee by Leon Casimir Bru

13" (33 cm). Bisque swivel head on kid-edged bisque shoulderplate, pale blue glass inset eyes with darker outer rims, dark eyeliner, painted lashes and feathered brows, accented nostrils and eye corners, closed mouth with delicate smile, accented lips, pierced ears, blonde mohair wig over cork pate, kid fashion body with square cut collarette, shapely adult female torso, gusset-jointing at hips and knees, kid upper arms, bisque forearms with sculpted fingers, defined knuckles and nails, antique green two piece gown with lace trim and black velvet bows, undergarments, leather boots, straw bonnet with black velvet bands. CONDITION: generally excellent. MARKS: C (head and shoulderplate). COMMENTS: Leon Casimir Bru, the "smiling" portrait model deposed by that firm in 1873. VALUE POINTS: rare and sought-after smiling poupee in appealing petite size, with original bisque-hand body, choice bisque, antique costume. $2800/3500

29. Very Beautiful French Bisque Poupee with Bisque Arms

17" (43 cm). Bisque swivel head on kid-edged bisque shoulderplate, dark blue glass enamel inset eyes, dark eyeliner encircles the eyecut, painted lashes, arched brows, accented eye corners, shaded nostrils, closed mouth, accented lips, ears pierced into the head, brunette mohair wig over cork pate, French kid fashion body with shapely waist and derriere, gusset jointed hips, kid-over-wooden dowel-jointed shoulders and elbows, bisque forearms with defined sculpting of nails and knuckles. CONDITION: generally excellent. COMMENTS: circa 1868. VALUE POINTS: with rarer body style, the beautiful poupee wears elaborate antique green silk two piece gown, undergarments, leather ankle boots, green velvet bonnet with lace trim, fur muff, antique jewelry including pearl necklace with cross, earrings, gilded folding lorgnette. $3500/4500

30. Exquisite French Bisque Bebe, A.T. by Thuillier with Original Costume

13" (33 cm). Bisque socket head, brown glass enamel inset eyes with spiral threading, painted lashes, brushstroked and feathered brows, accented nostrils and eye corners, closed mouth with slight definition of tongue tip between the shaded and outlined lips, pierced ears, blonde mohair wig over cork pate, French composition and wooden fully jointed body with straight wrists. CONDITION: generally excellent. MARKS: A. 4 T. COMMENTS: Thuillier, circa 1885. VALUE POINTS: exquisite and rare petite bebe with superb expression, bisque, and painting, original body and body finish, rose sateen frock appears original, antique lace bonnet, undergarments, stockings, and original brown leather shoes with silk rosettes and stars incised "A.T." in oval, and "4". A particular favorite of Mildred Seeley, the doll was featured in several books including *Fabulous French Bebes*. $20,000/30,000

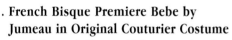

. **French Bisque Premiere Bebe by Jumeau in Original Couturier Costume**

12" (30 cm). Pressed bisque socket head, large brown glass enamel eyes in hand-cut eye sockets, painted lashes and brows, accented nostrils and eye corners, closed mouth with accented lips, pierced ears, blonde lambswool wig over cork pate, French composition and wooden eight-loose-ball-jointed body with straight wrists. CONDITION: generally excellent. MARKS: 4 (head) Jumeau Medaille d'Or Paris (body stamp). COMMENTS: Emile Jumeau, circa 1878. VALUE POINTS: outstanding preservation of the all-original bebe, wearing aqua silk frock and bonnet from the workshops of Ernestine Jumeau, original Jumeau undergarments, stockings, aqua leather shoes signed "E. Jumeau Med. d'or 1878 Paris", original earrings and necklace. An amusing story about Mildred Seeley's acquisition of the doll is told in her autobiography, *For the Love of Dolls and Roses*, page 75. $6500/8500

32. French Bisque Smiling Poupee by Bru with Depose Bru Wooden Body

15" (38 cm). Bisque swivel head on kid-edged bisque shoulderplate, almond-shaped pale blue glass enamel eyes with darker blue outer rims, painted lashes, arched feathered brows, accented nostrils and eye corners, closed mouth with accented lips, pierced ears, brunette mohair wig over cork pate, French all-wooden fully articulated body with dowel-jointing at shoulders, elbows, wrists, thighs, knees and ankles, and ball-swivel at waist, nicely costumed in peach silk gown with lace overlay, undergarments, silk slippers. CONDITION: generally excellent. MARKS: D. COMMENTS: Leon Casimir Bru, circa 1873, his portrait model inspired by the Empress Eugenie. VALUE POINTS: very beautiful poupee with choice bisque and painting, original deposed wooden Bru fashion body with original finish. $4000/5000

33. An Outstanding French Bisque Bebe by Leon Casimir Bru

25" (63 cm). Pressed bisque swivel head on kid-edged bisque shoulderplate with modelled bosom and shoulderblades, brown glass paperweight inset eyes with luminous depth and spiral threading, dark eyeliner encircles the eyecut, painted lashes, rose blushed eyeshadow, brushstroked and multi-feathered brows, accented eye corners, shaded nostrils, closed mouth with modelled tongue tip between the shaded and outlined lips, blonde mohair wig over cork pate, pierced ears, kid bebe body with plump torso, gusset-jointing at hips and knees, bisque forearms from above the elbows, separately sculpted fingers with defined knuckles and nails, antique ivory brocade silk dress, undergarments, leather shoes, bonnet, jewelry. CONDITION: generally excellent, muslin re-cover over kid on upper arms, patching at knees, right baby finger broken at knuckle. MARKS: Bru Jne 9. COMMENTS: Leon Casimir Bru, circa 1884. VALUE POINTS: outstanding example of the "golden age" Bru bebe with superb detail of sculpting, painting, quality of bisque, original body and wonderfully sculpted hands. The bebe was featured in the Seeley book *Fabulous French Bebes*. $18,000/24,000

34. Early English Wooden Doll Known as "Queen Anne"

13" (33 cm). Carved wooden head and torso with rounded facial modelling, elongated throat, rounded front torso with shapely waist, flat-back torso, carved nose, black enamel inset eyes, "dot" fringed lashes and brows, painted closed mouth and blushed cheek spots, brunette human hair, attached muslin arms, no legs, linen petticoat enclosing the leg area, antique silk brocade gown with panier skirt, lace trimmed collar and cap. CONDITION: good, original finish with some wear. COMMENTS: English, circa 1785, the style is known as "Queen Anne". VALUE POINTS: rare early doll with wonderful definition of personality, antique costume. $1200/1500

35. Extremely Rare French Wooden Court Lady Doll

14" (35 cm). One piece carved wooden head and torso portraying adult woman with elaborately arranged coiffure, carved facial features, painted large blue eyes in sculpted eye sockets, arched brows, aquiline nose, closed mouth with well-shaped lips, sculpted ears, adult female modelled body with highly detailed sculpting of female elements, hinge-jointed one piece legs, painted red shoes, muslin upper arms, wooden forearms and sculpted fingers, antique silk costume with elaborate trim. CONDITION: generally excellent. COMMENTS: Circa 1780, the doll was part of a series created to represent various personages of the French court of Louis XVI; the sculptor is unknown. VALUE POINTS: extremely rare doll with superbly sculpted hair is well-preserved and historically important. $3500/4500

36. A Companion Rare French Wooden Child

10" (25 cm). Carved wooden socket head with rounded childlike features, solid dome with tinted hair, carved and painted facial features, large blue upper glancing eyes, outlined eye sockets, arched thin-line brows, closed mouth with sculpted space between the lips, wooden torso with realistically sculpted male elements, wooden arms jointed at shoulders and elbows, one piece wooden legs with painted blue stockings and red shoes, early brocade and silk costume. CONDITION: doll is very good with original finish, costume somewhat frail. COMMENTS: Circa 1780, one of a series of wooden dolls created to represent particular persons of the court of Louis XVI; the sculptor is unknown. VALUE POINTS: very rare early wooden doll with appealing demeanor, important historical provenance. $2000/3000

37. Exceptionally Large German Bisque "Mein Liebling" by Kammer and Reinhardt
34" (86 cm). Bisque socket head, brown glass sleep eyes, painted curly lashes, dark eyeliner encircles the eyecuts, brushstroked and feathered brows, accented nostrils and eye corners, closed mouth with shaded and outlined lips, brunette human hair wig, composition and wooden ball-jointed body, antique white cotton dress, undergarments, leather shoes, straw bonnet. CONDITION: generally excellent. MARKS: K*R Simon & Halbig 117 80. COMMENTS: Kammer and Reinhardt, their model marketed as "Mein Susser Liebling" (my sweet darling). VALUE POINTS: the largest model of the desirable wistful-faced child with exceptional quality of bisque and painting, original body finish. $5500/7500

38. German Bisque Child by Kammer and Reinhardt

18" (46 cm). Bisque socket head, blue glass sleep and flirty eyes, painted lashes, dark eyeliner encircles the eyecut, feathered brows, accented nostrils, open mouth, shaded and outlined lips, four porcelain teeth, pierced ears, blonde human hair, composition and wooden ball-jointed body, antique silk dress, undergarments, leather shoes, straw bonnet. CONDITION: generally excellent. MARKS: K*R Simon & Halbig 46. COMMENTS: Kammer and Reinhardt, circa 1910. VALUE POINTS: beautiful example of child doll has well-functioning flirty eyes, original body and body finish, choice bisque. $600/900

39. German Bisque "Mein Liebling" by Kammer and Reinhardt

21" (55 cm). Bisque socket head, brown glass sleep eyes, dark eyeliner encircles the eyecut, painted curly lashes, brushstroked and feathered brows, accented nostrils, closed mouth with accent line between the shaded lips, blonde mohair wig, composition and wooden ball-jointed body. CONDITION: generally excellent. MARKS: K*R Simon & Halbig 117 55. COMMENTS: Kammer and Reinhardt, circa 1912. VALUE POINTS: considered among the most beautiful of the K*R character dolls, the wistful faced child has superb sculpting, fine dewy patina of bisque, original wig, original body and body finish, antique costume. $5000/6500

40. Rare German Bisque Character, 109, by Kammer and Reinhardt

12" (30 cm). Bisque socket head portraying an older child, painted blue eyes, black upper eyeliner and heavily modelled eyelids, one stroke brows, accented nostrils, closed mouth with very full lips accented by shading and decorative glaze, brunette mohair wig, composition and wooden ball-jointed body. CONDITION: generally excellent. MARKS: K*R 109 30. COMMENTS: Kammer and Reinhardt, from their art character series, circa 1910. VALUE POINTS: one of the rarer dolls from the art series, having very choice bisque and sculpting, original body and body finish, wearing antique folklore style costume. $3000/4000

41. German Bisque Pouty Character, 101, by Kammer and Reinhardt in Original Scottish Costume

12" (30 cm). Bisque socket head, painted facial features, small blue downcast eyes with upper eyeliner, one stroke brows, accented nostrils, closed mouth with pouty expression between the lips, blonde mohair wig, composition and wooden ball-jointed body. CONDITION: generally excellent. MARKS: K*R 30 101. COMMENTS: Kammer and Reinhardt, circa 1910, the model "Peter" from their art character series. VALUE POINTS: the wistful faced boy has original body, body finish, wig, and wears original well detailed Scottish costume. $1400/1800

42. German Bisque Pouty Character, "Gretchen", by Kammer and Reinhardt

19" (49 cm). Bisque socket head, painted facial features, large brown eyes with shaded detail and tiny white eyedots, heavily modelled eyelids with black upper eyeliner, one stroke tapered brows, accented nostrils, closed mouth with pouty expression on the full lips, brunette mohair wig, composition and wooden ball-jointed body. CONDITION: generally excellent. MARKS: K*R 114 49. COMMENTS: Kammer and Reinhardt, circa 1910, the model was presented as "Gretchen" in the company catalogs. VALUE POINTS: exceptional quality with most artistic painting, rarer brown eyes, glazed highlights of lips, original wig, body, body finish, antique folklore costume. The doll was featured in many of the Mildred Seeley books. $4000/5000

43. Pair, All Original German Bisque "Hans" and "Gretchen" by Kammer and Reinhardt

Each 7" (19 cm). Each has bisque socket head, painted facial features, blue eyes, one stroke brows, accented nostrils, closed mouth in pouty expression, mohair wig, composition five piece body with painted shoes and socks. CONDITION: generally excellent. MARKS: K*R 114 19. COMMENTS: Kammer and Reinhardt, circa 1915 from their art character series. VALUE POINTS: the smallest size of the character model retains fine quality of modelling, choice bisque, in unplayed with condition wearing original folklore costumes. $1800/2500

44. Superb French Brown-Complexioned Bebe, E.J., by Jumeau

17" (43 cm). Bisque socket head with cafe-au-lait complexion, amber brown glass inset eyes with spiral threading, dark eyeliner encircles the eyecut, painted lashes, black brushstroked brows with feathered highlights, accented nostrils, closed mouth with beautifully painted coral-shaded lips, impressed dimples, pierced ears, French composition and wooden fully jointed brown composition body with straight wrists. CONDITION: generally excellent. MARKS: Depose E 7 J (head) Jumeau Medaille d'Or Paris (head). COMMENTS: Emile Jumeau, circa 1885. VALUE POINTS: very rare model has superb complexion highlighted by lustrous patina, finest painting of features, original body and body finish that exactly matches facial complexion, original store costume of embroidered whitewear dress with layered undergarments including red woolen petticoat, red stockings, leather shoes with silk rosettes signed C.M., ruffled bonnet. $7500/9500

45. Early French Bisque
   Portrait Bebe by Jumeau

16" (40 cm). Pressed bisque socket head with very pale complexion, brown glass almond shaped inset eyes with spiral threading, mauve blushed eyeshadow, delicately painted lashes and brows with fringed detailing, accented eye corners, shaded nostrils, closed mouth with defined space between the shaded and outlined lips, pierced ears, blonde lambswool wig over cork pate, French composition and wooden eight-loose-ball-jointed body with straight wrists, antique sheer muslin frock with lace trim and matching cap, undergarments, white kid heeled shoes, original Jumeau earrings. CONDITION: generally excellent. MARKS: o. COMMENTS: Emile Jumeau, circa 1877. VALUE POINTS: one of the early model bebes, featuring exquisite portrait like modelling and painting, original body and body finish, lambswool wig.
$7500/9500

47. Very Rare French Bisque Doll, Model 223, by Jumeau
25" (63 cm). Bisque socket head, large brown glass paperweight inset eyes with spiral threading, dark eyeliner encircles the eyecut, lushly painted lashes, brushstroked brows with multi-feathered highlights, shaded nostrils, closed mouth with hint of smile, accent line between the shaded lips, separately modelled and pierced ears, brunette mohair wig over cork pate, French composition and wooden fully jointed body, red silk frock with matching wire-brimmed bonnet, undergarments, red knit stockings, black leather shoes with brown silk ribbons marked "Paris Depose 11" with bee symbol. CONDITION: generally excellent. MARKS: 223 (incised) Tete Jumeau Bte SGDG 11 (red stamp on head with artist checkmarks) Jumeau Diplome d'Honneur (paper label on torso). COMMENTS: Emile Jumeau, from his 200 series of character dolls, circa 1892. VALUE POINTS: very few examples of this doll are known to exist, the rarity enhanced by the beauty and quality of this example. The doll was featured on the cover of Mildred Seeley's book *Fabulous French Bebes*. $30,000/40,000

48. Early French Bisque Bebe by Francois Gaultier

19" (48 cm). Pressed bisque socket head with very pale complexion, large brown glass paperweight inset eyes with spiral threading, dark eyeliner encircles the eyecuts, painted lashes, arched feathered brows, accented eye corners and nostrils, closed mouth with modelled tongue tip between the pale outlined lips, pierced ears, blonde mohair wig over cork pate, French composition and wooden fully jointed body with plump limbs, straight wrists, pale green silk costume with lace trim, straw bonnet, undergarments, leather shoes. CONDITION: generally excellent, some body touch-up. MARKS: F. 8 G. (block letters). COMMENTS: Francois Gaultier, circa 1880. VALUE POINTS: wonderful example of the early model Gaultier bebe whose very plump face is contrasted by pale complexion and rich brown eyes. $4500/6500

49. French Bisque "Paris Bebe" by Jumeau

18" (46 cm). Bisque socket head with very full modelling of elongated cheeks, blue glass paperweight inset eyes, dark eyeliner encircles the eyecut, painted lashes, blushed eyeshadow, brushstroked and feathered brows, accented nostrils, closed mouth with defined space between the shaded and outlined lips, pierced ears, blonde mohair wig over cork pate, French composition and wooden fully jointed body. CONDITION: generally excellent. MARKS: Tete Depose Paris Bebe 8 (red stamp) 8 (incised). COMMENTS: Emile Jumeau, the unique model was created in 1892 after Jumeau won his lawsuit against Danel & Cie, winning the right to use the name "Paris Bebe". VALUE POINTS: a very appealing and distinctive expression on the historically significant doll, enhanced by very choice bisque with dewy patina, well defined features, original body and body finish, lovely costume of antique green silk with matching bonnet, undergarments, leather shoes. $4000/5500

50. French Bisque Poupee by Gaultier in Antique Gown
17" (45 cm). Bisque swivel head on kid-edged
bisque shoulderplate, pale blue glass inset eyes
with darker blue outer rims, painted lashes,
feathered brows, accented nostrils and eye
corners, closed mouth with accented lips,
pierced ears, brunette human hair over cork
pate, French kid fashion body with gusset
jointing, shapely torso, stitched and separated
fingers. CONDITION: generally excellent.
MARKS: 4. COMMENTS: Francois Gaultier, circa
1870. VALUE POINTS: beautiful poupee wears
antique green silk gown, undergarments, shoes,
watch and fob, bonnet. $2000/2500

51. German Bisque Flapper Fashion Doll, 1469, by Simon and Halbig

13" (33 cm). Bisque socket head with slender facial modelling, narrow blue glass sleep eyes, painted lashes, feathered brows, accented nostrils, closed mouth with accent line between the lips, elongated throat, pierced ears, brunette mohair wig, composition and wooden ball-jointed body with slender adult shape of flapper era, elongated slender limbs, feet modelled for wearing heels, wearing original muslin undergarments, black stockings, heeled shoes. CONDITION: generally excellent. MARKS: 1469 Simon & Halbig 2. COMMENTS: Simon & Halbig for Dressel, circa 1915. VALUE POINTS: the beautiful adult-featured doll is perfectly preserved with original wig, body, body finish, choice bisque. $3000/4000

52. Superb French Bisque Poupee, Size 9 by Jumeau

22" (56 cm). Bisque swivel head on kid-edged bisque shoulderplate, large blue glass paperweight inset eyes with spiral threading, painted curly lashes, brushstroked and feathered brows, accented eye corners, shaded nostrils, closed mouth with shaded and outlined lips, pierced ears, blonde mohair wig over cork pate, French kid fashion body with shapely torso, gusset-jointed elbows, hips and knees, stitched and separated fingers. CONDITION: generally excellent. MARKS: 9 (head, and artist checkmarks) Jumeau Medaille d'Or Paris (body). COMMENTS: Jumeau, circa 1878, the model for this poupee face transitioned into the portrait bebe; it appeared as poupee or fashion doll for a short time only. Both the poupee and bebe were shown at the Paris International Exposition of 1878, winning the "Medaille d'Or" award and signifying the firm's transition away from the poupee and toward the bebe. VALUE POINTS: superbly preserved example of the beautiful model, very sturdy body, original Jumeau muslin chemise beneath the elaborate gown made of antique silks, velvet bonnet, undergarments, boots. $4000/5000

53. French Bisque Bebe Steiner in Original Chemise

16" (40 cm). Bisque socket head, large blue glass enamel inset eyes, painted lashes, fringed brows, shaded nostrils, closed mouth with shaded and accented lips, pierced ears, blonde mohair wig over Steiner pate, French composition fully jointed body. CONDITION: generally excellent. MARKS: J. Steiner Bte SGDG Paris Fre A 9 (head) (original Steiner label on body). COMMENTS: Jules Steiner, circa 1890. VALUE POINTS: very pretty shy-faced bebe has exemplary bisque and painting, original signed body, original factory muslin chemise. $3000/3800

54. Outstanding French Bisque Bebe "A.T." by Thuillier

18" (46 cm). Pressed bisque swivel head on kid-edged bisque shoulderplate, distinctively shaped nose and chin point, full cheeks, almond shaped blue glass enamel inset eyes with spiral threading, dark eyeliner encircles the eyecut, dark painted lashes, mauve blushed eyeshadow, brushstroked and feathered brows, accented eye corners and shaded nostrils, closed mouth with shaded and outlined lips, pierced ears, blonde mohair wig over cork pate, French kid bebe body with square cut collarette, gusset-jointing at elbows, hips and knees, bisque forearms with separately sculpted fingers, defined knuckles and nails. CONDITION: generally excellent, some kid patching on original body. MARKS: A. 7 T. (head) A.T.7 (shoulderplate). COMMENTS: Andre Thuillier, circa 1880. VALUE POINTS: outstanding beauty of the very rare bebe whose quality of bisque and sculpting is enhanced further by artful painting, antique wig, original body with perfect and exquisite bisque hands, antique costume comprising ivory silk dress with soutache trim, undergarments, flower-trimmed bonnet, brown leather shoes signed "A.T.". $28,000/38,000

55. Wistful German Bisque Character, 7246, by Gebruder Heubach

13" (33 cm). Pink-tinted bisque socket head, blue glass sleep eyes, painted curly lashes, short feathered brows, accented nostrils and eye corners, closed mouth with glaze-accented lips in pouty expression, auburn human hair wig, composition and wooden ball-jointed body. CONDITION: generally excellent, hands repainted. MARKS: 7246 Heubach (in square) 4 Germany. COMMENTS: Gebruder Heubach, circa 1915. VALUE POINTS: fine quality of bisque and painting on the glass-eyed pouty child, with appealing antique white-wear costume, undergarments, leather shoes with coral pom-poms. $1100/1500

56. German All-Bisque "Bonnie Babe" by Georgene Averill

7" (18 cm). Solid domed bisque swivel head on chubby bisque toddler torso, sculpted short brown curly hair with forelock curls, brown glass sleep eyes, painted lashes, tinted brows, accented nostrils, open mouth posed in crooked smile, shaded lips, two porcelain lower teeth, loop-jointed bisque arms and legs, white painted socks and one-strap pink shoes. CONDITION: generally excellent, slight roughness at stringing arch, original vertical firing line on right leg. COMMENTS: "Bonnie Babe" designed by American artist Georgene Averill, produced in Germany, circa 1923. VALUE POINTS: wonderfully appealing all-bisque with deeply sculpted features, antique embroidered baby dress and bonnet. $700/900

57. German All-Bisque "Tynie Baby" by Horsman

8" (20 cm). Bisque socket head of chubby-faced baby on bisque baby torso, tiniest blue glass sleep eyes, painted lashes, tinted brows, accented nostrils, closed mouth with center accent line, blonde mohair wig, loop-jointed bisque arms and legs in bent-limb baby pose, bare feet. CONDITION: generally excellent. MARKS: c. 1924 by E.I. Horsman Co, Inc. Germany 43. COMMENTS: the doll was made exclusively for the Horsman firm of New York, and marketed as "Tynie Baby", circa 1924. VALUE POINTS: most appealing fretful baby expression is enhanced by choicest bisque and painting. $700/950

58. Rare German Bisque Character "The Singing Girl" by Gebruder Heubach

17" (43 cm). Pink tinted bisque socket head with sculpted short brown curly hair in loosely tousled arrangement, a modelled pink hair bow arranged at side of forehead, sculpted facial features, intaglio side-glancing blue eyes with large black pupils and white eyedots, black and incised eyeliner, accented nostrils, closed mouth modelled as though about to "sing", impressed dimples, composition and wooden ball-jointed body, antique whitewear and lace gown, undergarments, shoes and socks. CONDITION: generally excellent. MARKS: 7764 Heubach (in sunburst) Germany 6. COMMENTS: Gebruder Heubach, circa 1912. VALUE POINTS: the rarity of the model is rivaled by the outstanding quality of sculpting (appearing almost as though hand-pressed) and painting, original body and body finish. $3000/3800

60. French All-Bisque Mignonette with Jointed Elbows

5 1/2" (14 cm). Pale bisque swivel head on bisque torso, cobalt blue glass inset eyes, painted lashes and brows, accented nostrils, closed mouth with center accent line, blonde mohair wig, peg-jointed bisque arms with wooden ball-jointing at elbows, peg-jointed legs with bare feet, antique (very frail) ivory silk dress, muslin undergarments, lace cap. CONDITION: early hairline at back of head. COMMENTS: circa 1882, the ball-jointed body style was deposed by Schmitt et Fils. VALUE POINTS: rare early mignonette with jointed elbows, appealing expression. $900/1300

61. Exquisite French Bisque "Bebe Triste" by Emile Jumeau

29" (74 cm). Pressed bisque socket head with elongated facial modelling and very full cheeks, large blue glass paperweight inset eyes with luminous depth, dark eyeliner encircles the eyecut, dark painted lashes, rose

59. French Bisque Bebe Jumeau, Incised Depose Model, in Original Chemise

20" (51 cm). Pressed bisque socket head, blue glass paperweight inset eyes, painted lashes, brushstroked brows, mauve blushed eyeshadow, accented eye corners and nostrils, closed mouth with modelled space between the outlined and shaded lips, separated applied pierced ears, blonde mohair wig over cork pate, French composition and wooden eight-loose-ball-jointed body with straight wrists. CONDITION: generally excellent. MARKS: Depose X 9 (incised) Jumeau Medaille d'Or Paris (torso). COMMENTS: Emile Jumeau, circa 1885. VALUE POINTS: one of the rarer signature models of Jumeau has deeply sculpted features, exquisite painting of features, original body and body finish, antique extended-length mohair wig, original muslin Jumeau chemise, black net stockings, white leather shoes. $6000/7500

blushed eyeshadow, brushstroked and multi-feathered brows, accented eye corners, shaded nostrils, closed mouth with modelled space between the shaded and outlined lips, impressed dimples at corners of mouth, separately applied pierced ears, blonde mohair wig over cork pate, French composition and wooden fully jointed body with very plump limbs. CONDITION: generally excellent, some minor body wear. MARKS: 13 (incised) Bebe Jumeau Diplome d'honneur (paper label on torso). COMMENTS: Emile Jumeau, circa 1885. VALUE POINTS: outstanding quality of sculpting and finest creamy bisque enhanced by artful painting, lovely antique costume, signed Bebe Jumeau shoes. The doll was featured in a full-page photograph in *Fabulous French Bebes* by Mildred Seeley.
$11,000/13,000

62. English Poured Wax Baby from Hamley's

13" (33 cm). Poured rosy wax shoulderhead modelled turned to the right, blue glass enamel inset eyes, incised eyeliner, feathered brows, accented nostrils and eye corners, closed mouth with downcast lips, delicate mohair inserted into scalp, original softly-stuffed muslin body with stitch-jointing, wax lower arms and legs, bare feet. CONDITION: generally excellent. MARKS: Hamley's, 612 Oxford Street, London (body stamp). COMMENTS: circa 1880, the doll was sold from the famous London toy shop of Hamley's. VALUE POINTS: most endearing petite size wax doll with wistful expression, antique costume, signed body. $800/1100

**63. Exquisite German Bisque Fashion Lady
with Twill & Wooden Body by Simon and Halbig**

17" (43 cm). Pale bisque swivel head on kid-edged bisque shoulderplate, blue glass enamel inset eyes, dark eyeliner encircles the eyecut, painted lashes, feathered brows, accented eye corners, shaded nostrils, closed mouth with accent lines on pale lips, ears pierced into head, blonde mohair wig, twill-over-wooden body with shapely torso, dowel-jointed shoulders, elbows, hips, knees and ankles, bisque forearms and sculpted fingers, pale green muslin dress and apron, lace collar, undergarments. CONDITION: generally excellent, right thumb restored. COMMENTS: Simon and Halbig, circa 1880. VALUE POINTS: rare model in fine larger size with exquisite modelling and decoration, superb body. $3500/4500

**64. Outstanding French Bisque Bebe,
Figure C, by Jules Steiner**

29" (74 cm). Pale bisque socket head with rounded facial modelling, perfectly oval blue glass enamel inset eyes, painted dark lashes with "dot" highlights, rose blushed eyeshadow, thickly fringed brows, accent dots at eye corners, shaded nostrils, closed mouth with outlined shaded lips, impressed lip corners, dimpled and blushed chin, well-detailed blushed ears with pierced earlobes, long wheat blonde human hair wig in ringlet curls over Steiner pate, French composition fully jointed body with semi-cupped separated fingers. CONDITION: generally excellent. MARKS: Figure C, No.8 J. Steiner Bte SGDG Paris (incised, head) (black caduceus stamp on torso). COMMENTS: Jules Steiner, circa 1884. VALUE POINTS: an outstanding early model Steiner bebe with finest quality of bisque and painting, original body and body finish, antique silk costume with encrusted seed decoration, undergarments, bonnet, leather shoes. A particular favorite of Mildred Seeley, the doll was displayed prominently in her home for nearly two decades. $8000/11,000

65. A Superb All-Original German Bisque Chinese Baby, 243, by Kestner

13" (33 cm). Amber tinted bisque socket head, brown glass sleep eyes, painted long curly upper lashes, black feathered brows, accented nostrils and eye corners, open mouth, shaded and accented lips, two porcelain upper teeth, tongue, black mohair wig over plaster pate, amber tinted composition five piece baby body. CONDITION: generally excellent. MARKS: F made in Germany 10 243 JDK. COMMENTS: Kestner, circa 1915. VALUE POINTS: superb portrait doll whose facial model was used for this presentation only, exemplary and perfectly preserved condition, choicest bisque and painting, original elaborate silk costume created exclusively for Gump's of San Francisco circa 1915 includes beaded and embroidered decorations. $5500/7500

66. A Petite Black-Complexioned Bebe by Jules Steiner

10" (25 cm). Bisque socket head with dark brown complexion, brown glass enamel inset eyes, black painted lashes, black feathered brows, accented nostrils, closed mouth with coral painted lips, pierced ears, black mohair wig, French brown composition fully jointed body. CONDITION: generally excellent. MARKS: J. Steiner Bte SGDG Fre A 3 (head) (original Steiner 1889 paper label on back torso). COMMENTS: Jules Steiner, circa 1889. VALUE POINTS: the brown complexioned bebe has superb lustrous patina of complexion, original body and body finish, antique muslin chemise dress. $3000/3800

67. Rare French Bisque Bebe Bru with Mulatto Complexion

17" (43 cm). Bisque socket head with light brown mulatto complexion, on original light brown composition shoulderplate, amber brown glass enamel inset eyes, dark painted lashes, brown thick brushstroked brows with feathered highlights, accented nostrils, closed mouth with accented plum-tinted lips, upturned lip corners, pierced ears, black fleecy wig over cork pate, Bru kid body with scalloped edge collarette, kid over metal upper arms, Chevrot-hinged hips, wooden lower legs, bisque lower arms with separately sculpted fingers, lovely costume of plaid taffeta with black silk apron, cotton blouse, undergarments, bead earrings, antique turquoise leather shoes. CONDITION: generally excellent. MARKS: Bru Jne 7. COMMENTS: Bru, circa 1888. VALUE POINTS: splendid mulatto complexion of face and hands is heightened with lustrous patina, beautifully painted features, original body, perfect hands. The doll was featured in a full-page photograph in *Fabulous French Bebes* by Mildred Seeley. $9000/13,000

"To reflect its true history, a doll and its costumes must be preserved."

Mildred Seeley in *Doll Costuming*

68. German Bisque Toddler, 247, by Kestner

15" (38 cm). Bisque socket head, brown glass sleep eyes, painted curly lashes, incised eyeliner, short feathered brows, accented nostrils and eye corners, open mouth, shaded and accented lips, two porcelain upper teeth, brunette mohair wig over plaster pate, composition and wooden ball-jointed toddler body with side-hip jointing. CONDITION: generally excellent. MARKS: F made in Germany 10 247 JDK 10. COMMENTS: Kestner, circa 1915. VALUE POINTS: appealing character toddler has wonderfully sculpted features, original wig, pate, body, body finish, antique schoolboy costume. $800/1100

69. Petite German Bisque Child by Kestner

10" (25 cm). Bisque socket head, grey glass sleep eyes, painted long curly lashes, brushstroked and feathered brows, accented nostrils, open mouth, accented lips, four porcelain teeth, blonde mohair wig over plaster pate, composition and wooden ball-jointed body. CONDITION: generally excellent. MARKS: 4. COMMENTS: Kestner, circa 1900. VALUE POINTS: appealing petite child with fine quality bisque, original body and body finish, antique costume. $600/900

70. German Bisque Character, 143, by Kestner

14" (35 cm). Bisque socket head, blue glass sleep eyes, painted lashes, brushstroked brows, accented nostrils and eye corners, open mouth, outlined lips, two porcelain upper teeth, blonde mohair wig over plaster pate, composition and wooden ball-jointed body. CONDITION: generally excellent. MARKS: B made in Germany 6 143 (head) Germany (body). COMMENTS: Kestner, circa 1915. VALUE POINTS: pretty demi-character with excellent sculpting, original body and body finish, elongated mohair wig, antique embroidered costume, undergarments, straw bonnet, leather shoes. $600/900

71. Petite German Bisque Character, 206, with Original Labelled Costume

12" (30 cm). Bisque socket head, brown glass sleep eyes, painted lashes, incised eyeliner, short feathered brows, accented nostrils, closed mouth with accent line between the lips, brunette mohair wig with side-braids over plaster pate, composition and wooden ball-jointed body. CONDITION: generally excellent. MARKS: e 206 3 made in Germany. COMMENTS: Kestner, circa 1915. VALUE POINTS: rare model with wonderful expression, choice bisque, original wig, pate, body, body finish, wearing antique embroidered dress, undergarments, shoes, and socks. The dress has original label "Smart Set", a label used by the Weston and Wells Co. of Philadelphia who advertised in Playthings, 1911, that they had 100 different doll's dresses in the latest styles. $3000/4000

72. Rare German Bisque Dimpled Character, 9681, by Gebruder Heubach

14" (35 cm). Pink tinted bisque socket head, brown glass sleep eyes, painted lashes, feathered brows, accented nostrils and eye corners, open mouth with very slightly parted lips, brunette mohair bobbed wig, composition and wooden ball-jointed toddler body with side-hip jointing. CONDITION: generally excellent, right thumb broken. MARKS: 9681 2 Heubach (in square). COMMENTS: Gebruder Heubach, circa 1918. VALUE POINTS: rare previously undocumented model with wonderful expression, uniquely shaped mouth, impressed cheek and mouth dimples, toddler body with original finish, antique Tyrolean costume. $2500/3500

74. French Bisque Taufling Baby with Bisque Body Elements

19" (48 cm). Solid domed bisque shoulderhead with rounded facial modelling, almond shaped blue enamel glass inset eyes, painted lashes, feathered brows, accented nostrils and eye corners, closed mouth with outlined pale lips, unpierced ears, blonde mohair fleecy wig, muslin midriff and upper arms and legs, bisque lower torso and lower arms and legs, bisque feet. CONDITION: fingers and left foot repaired, muslin recovered. COMMENTS: Jules Steiner, circa 1870, his early model taufling bebe known as "Motschmann". VALUE POINTS: rarer early version of the Steiner taufling with artfully painted bisque, antique baby costume. $2200/2700

75. Beautiful Large French Bisque Bebe, Series C, by Jules Steiner

32" (81 cm). Bisque socket head with rounded facial modelling, very pale complexion with delicate blushing, blue glass sleep eyes that operate from lever at back of head, painted lashes, incised eyeliner, rose blushed eyeshadow, brushstroked and feathered brows, shaded nostrils, closed mouth with outlined lips, defined space between the lips, pierced ears, brunette mohair wig, French composition and wooden fully jointed body. CONDITION: generally excellent. MARKS: Sie C. 7 (incised) J. SteinerBte SGDG J. Bourgoin (red ink script). (original Steiner caduceus stamp on body) (eyes signed J. Steiner). COMMENTS: Jules Steiner, circa 1882. VALUE POINTS: stunningly beautiful quality of bisque and painting on the large bebe with original body and body finish, impressed dimples on chin, philtrum and lip corners, signed lever sleep eyes, lovely antique costume. $7500/9500

76. French Mechanical Singing Bird Attributed to Bontemps

20" cage (51 cm). A metal birdcage with gilded floral designs on the ornamental base (which disguises the mechanism) contains a brass balancing rod upon which is perched a feathered bird. When wound and lever released the bird realistically flutters its wings, moves its head from side to side, beak opens and closes and the bird sings. Stamped "France" on base. Attributed to Bontemps, circa 1910. $1000/1400

73. French Bisque Bebe Steiner, Series C

28" (71 cm). Bisque socket head with rounded facial modelling, large blue glass paperweight inset eyes, painted lashes with "dot" highlights, rose blushed eyeshadow, brushstroked fringed brows, accented eye corners, shaded nostrils, closed mouth with shaded and outlined lips, blushed cheeks and dimpled chin, blushed pierced ears, (worn) original lambswool wig over Steiner pate, French composition fully jointed body. CONDITION: generally excellent, body repainted. MARKS: Sie C 6 (incised) Bourgoin Bte SGDG Paris (red lettering). COMMENTS: Jules Steiner, circa 1882. VALUE POINTS: the early model bebe has very beautiful modelling and painting, original body, costumed in antique baby dress, undergarments, bonnet. $5000/6500

77. French Bisque Automaton "Smiling Girl with Playful Kitten" by Leopold Lambert

20" (51 cm) overall. A bisque headed girl with unusual character features portraying a happy child with wide beaming smile, brown glass paperweight inset eyes, painted lashes, widely arched brushstroked brows with decorative glaze, accented nostrils, closed mouth with shaded and accented lips, defined tongue, row of sculpted teeth, pierced ears, blonde mohair wig over cork pate, carton torso and legs, wire upper arms, bisque forearms and hands, is standing upon a velvet covered base which contains clockwork and musical mechanisms. A rod, protruding from her torso, supports a wicker tray in which is arranged a little kitten tucked among silk flowers. When wound, music plays and a series of amusing movements occur: the girl turns her head from side to side, then nods, appears to choose a flower, while the kitten playfully jumps toward her hand. CONDITION: generally excellent. MARKS: 203 (and artist checkmarks on head). LB (key). COMMENTS: Leopold Lambert, utilizing rare character portrait head designed by Jumeau for Lambert's automata, circa 1890. VALUE POINTS: very rare character model with wonderfully defined features, amusing automaton action, original peach silk costume. $8000/12,000

77A. Very Beautiful French Bisque Bebe by Schmitt et Fils

17" (43 cm). Pressed bisque socket head with rounded facial modelling, bright blue glass enamel inset eyes with spiral threading, mauve blushed eyeshadow, delicately painted lashes and brows, accented nostrils and eye corners, closed mouth with outlined lips, pierced ears, blonde mohair wig, French composition and wooden eight-loose-ball-jointed body with straight wrists and flat-cut derriere. CONDITION: generally excellent. MARKS: Bte SGDG 2 (head) (shield mark on derriere). COMMENTS: Schmitt et Fils, circa 1880. VALUE POINTS: very beautiful example of Bebe Schmitt whose brilliant blue eyes complement the delicately tinted bisque, original body and body finish, antique silk twill and red velvet dress, undergarments, shoes and socks. The doll was a particular favorite of Mildred Seeley and was featured in her book *Fabulous French Bebes*. $9000/13,000

78. Petite French Bisque Bebe Steiner, Series C

12" (30 cm). Bisque socket head with rounded facial modelling, blue glass sleep eyes that operate from lever at back of head, painted lashes, feathered brows, rose blushed eyeshadow, accented nostrils and eye corners, closed mouth with accented lips, pierced ears, blonde mohair wig over Steiner pate, French composition fully jointed body, nicely costumed in pale green silk, undergarments, silk bonnet, kid slippers. CONDITION: generally excellent. MARKS: Sie C 2/o (incised) J. Steiner Bte SGDG J. Bourgoin Succ. (red ink script) (caduceus stamp on body) (eyes signed J. Steiner). COMMENTS: Jules Steiner, circa 1884. VALUE POINTS: rare petite size of the early bebe has superb bisque and painting, original signed body and eyes. $3000/3800

79. Very Beautiful French Bisque Bebe "A.T." by Thuillier

24" (61 cm). Pressed bisque socket head, large blue glass paperweight inset eyes, dark eyeliner encircles the eyecut, painted dark curly lashes, rose blushed eyeshadow, brushstroked and multi-feathered brows, accented eye corners, shaded nostrils, closed mouth with defined space between the shaded and outlined lips, pierced ears, wheat blonde mohair wig over cork pate, French composition and wooden fully jointed body with straight wrist, antique white dress with cutwork bodice, undergarments, leather shoes, ruffled bonnet. CONDITION: generally excellent. MARKS: A. 12 T. COMMENTS: Andre Thuillier, circa 1885. VALUE POINTS: rarely found large and beautiful bebe with exceptional quality of sculpting, bisque and painting, especially fine detail of painting of lips and blush. $25,000/32,000

80. An All Original German Bisque Child by Heinrich Handwerck

28" (71 cm). Bisque socket head, large brown glass sleep eyes, mohair lashes, painted lower lashes, dark eyeshadow, brushstroked brows with glazed highlights and feathering, accented nostrils, open mouth, shaded and accented lips, four porcelain teeth, pierced ears, blonde mohair wig, composition and wooden ball-jointed body. CONDITION: generally excellent. MARKS: Heinrich Handwerck Simon & Halbig 5 (head) Heinrich Handwerck (body). COMMENTS: Handwerck, circa 1900. VALUE POINTS: the pretty dolly-faced model has original body, body finish, mohair wig, antique multi-layered costume. $800/1100

81. German Bisque Child by Heinrich Handwerck

29" (74 cm). Bisque socket head, blue glass sleep eyes, painted lashes, brushstroked and feathered brows, accented nostrils, open mouth, shaded and outlined lips, three porcelain teeth, pierced ears, brunette mohair wig, composition and wooden ball-jointed body. CONDITION: generally excellent, one tooth missing. MARKS: Germany Heinrich Handwerck Simon & Halbig 6 (head) Heinrich Handwerck Germany (body). COMMENTS: Handwerck, circa 1910. VALUE POINTS: pretty child with original body, body finish, wig, well-detailed antique costume. $600/800

82. German Bisque Character, 143, by Kestner

27" (68 cm). Bisque socket head, large blue glass sleep eyes, painted lashes, incised eyeliner, brushstroked and feathered brows with decorative glaze, accented eye corners and nostrils, open mouth, shaded and outlined lips, two porcelain upper teeth, dimpled chin, brunette mohair wig over plaster pate, composition and wooden ball-jointed body, woolen plaid boy's suit and cap, black stockings, leather ankle boots. CONDITION: generally excellent. MARKS: L made in Germany 15 143 (head) Germany (body). COMMENTS: Kestner, circa 1910. VALUE POINTS: rare larger model of 143 character has very choice bisque and painting, original body and body finish. $1100/1400

82A. German Bisque Child by Kestner

12" (30 cm). Bisque socket head, blue glass sleep eyes, painted lashes, brushstroked brows, accented eye corners and nostrils, open mouth, outlined lips, four porcelain teeth, blonde mohair wig over plaster pate, composition and wooden ball-jointed body, nicely costumed. CONDITION: generally excellent. MARKS: B made in Germany 6. COMMENTS: Kestner, circa 1900. VALUE POINTS: beautiful little child with choice bisque, original wig, pate, body, body finish. $600/800

83. Large German Bisque Character, 2072, from Bruno Schmidt

32" (81 cm). Bisque socket head, brown glass sleep eyes, painted curly lashes, incised eyeliner, mohair lashes, curvy feathered brows, accented nostrils and eye corners, closed mouth with shaded and outlined lips, brunette human hair, composition and wooden ball-jointed body with side-hip jointing, antique white cotton dress with butterfly cutwork, undergarments, leather shoes. CONDITION: generally excellent. MARKS: B.P.(crossed swords) BSW (in heart) 2072. COMMENTS: made by Bahr and Proschild for Bruno Schmidt, circa 1910. VALUE POINTS: unusually large size child has excellent detail of sculpting, choice bisque and painting, original body and body finish. $3000/3800

84. French Bisque Poupee by Francois Gaultier

22" (56 cm). Bisque swivel head on kid-edged bisque shoulderplate, blue glass enamel inset eyes with spiral threading, dark eyeliner encircles the eyecut, painted lashes, feathered arched brows, accented eye corners, shaded nostrils, closed mouth with detailed accents on pale lips, pierced ears, brunette mohair wig over cork pate, French kid gusset jointed body with stitched and separated fingers, shapely torso, lovely velvet and silk costume with long train, bonnet, undergarments, wooden-handled parasol. CONDITION: generally excellent, some minor patching on body. MARKS: 6 (head) F.G. 6 (shoulderplate). COMMENTS: Francois Gaultier, circa 1870. VALUE POINTS: especially beautiful quality of bisque and painting on the large poupee. $3000/3500

85. Beautiful French Bisque Portrait Bebe by Jumeau

18" (46 cm). Pressed bisque socket head, large almond shaped dark grey glass inset eyes with prominent spiral threading, dark eyeliner encircles the eyecut, painted lashes, mauve blushed eyeshadow, feathered brows, accented nostrils and eye corners, closed with defined space between the shaded and outlined lips, pierced ears, blonde human hair over cork pate, French composition and wooden eight-loose-ball-jointed body with straight wrists, tea blue silk costume and decorated straw bonnet. CONDITION: generally excellent, minute flake at bottom left eye rim. MARKS: 9 (head) Jumeau Medaille d'Or Paris (body). COMMENTS: Emile Jumeau, circa 1878. VALUE POINTS: early portrait bebe with dramatic and beautiful eyes, choice bisque and painting, original body and body finish. $6000/8000

86. French Bisque Portrait Bebe by Emile Jumeau

16" (40 cm). Pressed bisque socket head, wide almond shaped grey enamel glass inset eyes with prominent spiral threading, dark eyeliner encircles the eyecut, painted lashes, brushstroked and feathered brows, mauve blushed eyeshadow, accented eye corners, shaded nostrils, closed mouth with outlined shaded lips, pierced ears, brunette human hair over cork pate, French composition and wooden eight-loose-ball-jointed body with straight wrists. CONDITION: generally excellent, knee balls have worn paint. MARKS: 1. COMMENTS: Emile Jumeau, circa 1877. VALUE POINTS: the earliest period bebe has stunningly beautiful bisque and painting, original body and body finish. $6000/8000

87. Rare French Bisque Bebe by Petit et Dumoutier

19" (48 cm). Bisque socket head with plump rounded facial modelling, brown glass enamel inset eyes, painted lashes, brushstroked and multi-feathered brows, accented nostrils and eye corners, closed mouth with outlined lips, pierced ears, blonde mohair wig over cork pate, French composition and wooden fully jointed body with pewter hands, ivory silk costume with embroidered yoke, undergarments, antique plush-trimmed bonnet, leather shoes signed "Paris 2". CONDITION: generally excellent, finish a bit worn on hands. MARKS: P. 2 D. COMMENTS: Petit & Dumoutier, circa 1885. VALUE POINTS: bebes by this firm are rarely found, especially with their unique original bodies as this has; beautiful bisque and painting. $7000/10,000

88. French Bisque Bebe "Pan" by Henri Delcroix

26" (66 cm). Bisque socket head with long-faced modelling and very full cheeks, large blue glass paperweight inset eyes, dark eyeliner encircles the eyecut, dark painted lashes, incised eyeliner, rose blushed eyeshadow, brushstroked brows with feathered highlights, shaded nostrils, closed mouth with heart-shaped upper lip, upturned lip corners, pierced ears, brunette mohair wig over cork pate, French composition and wooden eight-loose-ball-jointed body with straight wrists. CONDITION: generally excellent. MARKS: Pan (in block) 11. COMMENTS: Henri Delcroix, who registered the trademark for "Pan" in 1887. VALUE POINTS: superb large size of the rare bebe has dramatic features enhanced by fine painting, original body finish, lovely lace costume. A particular favorite of Mildred Seeley, the doll was featured in *Fabulous French Bebes* in which the author relates an amusing story about the origin of her quest for the Pan doll. $8000/12,000

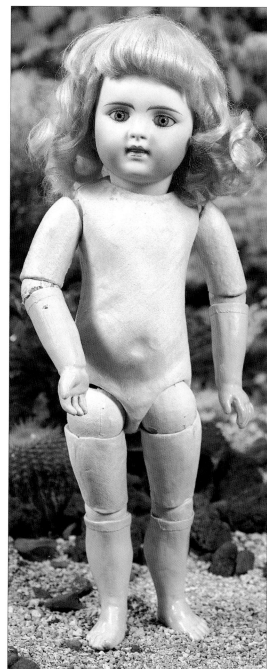

89. German Bisque Child, 929, by Simon and Halbig

17" (43 cm). Solid domed bisque socket head with elongated facial modelling, small grey glass inset eyes with spiral threading, dark painted lashes, brushstroked and feathered brows, accented nostrils and eye corners, closed mouth, accented lips, blonde mohair wig, Sonneberg composition and wooden fully jointed body with straight wrists, antique dress, bonnet, undergarments, shoes and stockings. CONDITION: generally excellent, some body retouch, eyes reset. MARKS: 929 S 9 H. COMMENTS: Simon and Halbig, circa 1885. VALUE POINTS: rare early model with compelling expression, choice bisque with luminous complexion. $1800/2300

90. Early German Bisque Child by Simon and Halbig with Rare Body

14" (35 cm). Bisque socket head with rounded facial modelling, small bright blue glass enamel inset eyes with spiral threading, painted lashes, lightly blushed eyeshadow, delicately feathered brows, accented nostrils, closed mouth with defined space between the outlined lips, pierced ears, blonde mohair wig, composition and wooden eight-loose-ball-jointed body with unusual sateen-over-composition on torso and upper arms and legs, unusual low-slung derriere, shapely ankles, antique silk dress and leather slippers included. CONDITION: generally excellent. COMMENTS: Simon and Halbig, circa 1880. VALUE POINTS: very rare model whose facial beauty is rivalled by the distinctive early body. $2000/2500

91. Early German Bisque Child
Attributed to Simon & Halbig

16" (40 cm). Bisque socket head with rounded facial modelling, blue glass inset eyes, dark eyeliner encircles the eyecut, delicately painted lashes, brushstroked brows with feathered detail, accented nostrils and eye corners, closed mouth with accent line between the lips, pierced ears, blonde mohair wig, early composition and wooden eight-loose-ball-jointed body with straight wrists, wearing blue and white sailor costume. CONDITION: generally excellent, body finish worn. MARKS: 4. COMMENTS: attributed to Simon & Halbig, circa 1884. VALUE POINTS: very beautiful face on the early model with choice bisque and painting. $2000/2500

92. German Bisque Child,
939, by Simon and Halbig

17" (43 cm). Bisque socket head with long-faced modelling, small blue glass enamel inset eyes with spiral threading, painted lashes, brushstroked brows, accented nostrils and eye corners, closed mouth with accented lips, pierced ears, brunette mohair wig, composition and wooden eight-loose-ball-jointed body with straight wrists, nicely costumed. CONDITION: generally excellent. MARKS: S 10 H 939. COMMENTS: Simon and Halbig, circa 1885. VALUE POINTS: pretty closed mouth child with beautiful eyes, choice bisque and painting. $1200/1700

94. Very Beautiful and Large French Bisque Bebe by Leon Casimir Bru

30" (76 cm). Bisque swivel head on kid-edged bisque shoulderplate with modelled bosom and shoulderblades, very deep blue glass paperweight inset eyes, dark eyeliner encircles the eyecut, painted lashes, mauve blushed eyeshadow, brushstroked and multi-feathered brows, accented eye corners, shaded nostrils, closed mouth with shaded and outlined lips, modelled tongue tip between the lips, pierced ears, blonde mohair wig over cork pate, French kid body with gusset-jointing at hips and knees, kid over metal upper arms, bisque forearms with separately sculpted fingers, defined knuckles and nails, antique lace bonnet and jacket, second costume of blue silks included. CONDITION: an old hairline extends from left eye corner down the outside of cheek. MARKS: Bru Jne 12 (head) Bru Jne (left shoulderplate) No. 12 (right shoulderplate). COMMENTS: Leon Casimir Bru, circa 1882, the earliest period of the Bru Jne model. VALUE POINTS: the large size allows full expression of the splendid model including defined modelling around the mouth and unusually full definition of cleavage, superb bisque and luminous eyes, original sturdy body, perfect hands. $12,000/18,000

93. Exquisite Petite French Bisque Bebe Bru, Size 1

11" (28 cm). Bisque swivel head on kid-edged bisque shoulderplate, amber brown glass paperweight inset eyes, painted long lashes, brushstroked and multi-feathered brows, accented nostrils and eye corners, closed mouth with accent line between the full lips, pierced ears, blonde mohair wig over cork pate, French kid body with Chevrot hinged hips, kid-over-metal upper arms, bisque forearms with separately sculpted fingers, wooden lower legs, scalloped kid collarette. CONDITION: generally excellent. MARKS: Bru Jne 1 (head) Bru Jne (left shoulderplate) No.1 (right shoulderplate), (original paper label on torso). COMMENTS: Leon Casimir Bru, circa 1885. VALUE POINTS: exquisite size 1 Bru bebe with compelling expression, choice bisque, original labelled body, perfect bisque hands, antique costume which may be original. $11,000/15,000

95. Exceptionally Large French Bisque Bebe Jumeau, Size 16

36" (91 cm). Bisque socket head, blue glass paperweight inset eyes in smaller eyecuts, dark eyeliner encircles the eyecut, painted lashes, brushstroked and multi-feathered brows with decorative glaze, accented eye corners, shaded nostrils, closed mouth with defined space between the shaded and outlined lips, separately applied pierced ears, blonde human hair over cork pate, French composition and wooden fully jointed body with working pull-string "mama" crier. CONDITION: generally excellent. MARKS: Depose Tete Jumeau Bte SGDG 16 (and artist checkmarks). COMMENTS: Emile Jumeau, circa 1886. VALUE POINTS: rarer large size with well defined features, choice bisque, original body and body finish, antique maroon silk dress and velvet bonnet, undergarments. $7000/9000

96. French Bisque Bebe Steiner

29" (74 cm). Bisque socket head, large dark blue glass paperweight inset eyes, dark eyeliner encircles the eyecut, lushly painted lashes, widely arched brushstroked and feathered brows, accented eye corners, shaded nostrils, closed mouth with very full outlined lips, pierced ears, brunette mohair wig over cork pate, French composition fully jointed body. CONDITION: generally excellent. MARKS: A 12 Paris (incised) Le Parisien (red stamp). COMMENTS: Steiner, circa 1890. VALUE POINTS: pretty large model Steiner bebe has original Steiner body, wears antique burgundy silk dress, bonnet, undergarments, black stockings, black leather shoes. $3500/4500

97. French Bisque Character, 233, by SFBJ

23" (58 cm). Solid domed bisque socket head with modelling detail of unpainted hair under the wig, brown glass inset eyes in very narrow squinting expression, brown single stroke brows, brown curly lashes, accented nostrils, closed mouth modelled as though open in crying expression, modelled tongue, modelled row of upper teeth and two lower teeth, auburn mohair wig, French composition and wooden fully jointed body, mauve silk costume, antique leather shoes. CONDITION: generally excellent, tiny original firing point on nose. MARKS: SFBJ 233 Paris 8. COMMENTS: SFBJ, circa 1910, from their 200 series of character dolls, continuing the series begun by Jumeau in 1892. The doll was modelled to be completed with painted hair, flocked hair, or wig. VALUE POINTS: rare model with superb definition of sculpting depicting crying wrinkles around the eyes and mouth, superb bisque with dewy patina, enhancing glaze on teeth, original body and body finish. $5000/7000

98. A Staircase of German All-Bisque Kewpies

2"-6" (5-15 cm). Ten Kewpies in various styles are posed on a staircase in manner designed to accentuate their body styles or activities. Included is Kewpie with guitar standing aside a vase, seated Kewpie with book, tiny Kewpie boutonniere, Kewpie Farmer, four standing Kewpies with jointed arms, seated Kewpie with folded arms on yellow chair, and Kewpie Traveller with umbrella and valise. Each is appropriately marked, some with "c" in black circle stamp, others with paper label or incised "O'Neill". All in excellent condition. The Kewpies were designed by Rose O'Neill, produced in Germany, circa 1915. $1600/1900

99. German All Bisque Baby

8 1/2" (21 cm). One piece bisque head and torso, solid domed with painted baby hair, painted facial features, blue eyes, red and black upper eyeliner, single stroke brows, accented nostrils, closed mouth modelled as though open, outlined lips, loop-jointed bisque arms and legs in bent baby pose. CONDITION: generally excellent. MARKS: 5 (inside arms and legs). COMMENTS: Hertwig, circa 1915. VALUE POINTS: large all bisque doll with excellent definition of modelling. $400/500

100. German All Bisque Kewpie on a Swing

2 1/2" h (6 cm). bisque figure. One piece bisque figure of Kewpie in seated position, posed on a blue swinging hammock, with right arm outstretched, left arm holding a book, with topknot, blue wings, side glancing googly eyes. Marked "c" with black stamp in circle, and original O'Neill, Germany paper label. Designed by Rose O'Neill, produced in Germany, circa 1920. Excellent condition. $300/400

101. German All Bisque Kewpie with Black Cat

3 1/2" (9 cm). One piece bisque figure of seated Kewpie, head turned to the side, modelled topknot, blue wings, side-glancing googly eyes, arms modelled away from body, ankles crossed, with black cat walking across Kewpie's lap. Marked "c" with black stamp in circle. Designed by Rose O'Neill, produced in Germany, circa 1915. Excellent condition, minute flake at cat tail tip. $200/300

102. German All Bisque Seated Baby by Gebruder Heubach

5" (13 cm) seated. One piece all bisque figure of seated baby with head turned to the side and surprised expression on face, painted hair with topknot, wide-open intaglio eyes, black upper eyeliner, pug nose with accent dots, single stroke brows, "O" shaped mouth, arms posed away from body with spread fingers, crossed ankles. Excellent condition. Marked "Heubach" in square. Germany, circa 1920. $400/500

103. German Bisque Baby "Hilda" by Kestner

18" (46 cm). Solid domed bisque socket head with delicately painted blonde baby hair, forelock curls, brown glass sleep eyes, painted curly lashes, short feathered brows, accented nostrils and eye corners, open mouth, two porcelain upper teeth, modelled tongue, composition bent limb baby body, antique costume. CONDITION: generally excellent, one baby finger repaired. MARKS: JDK Ges Gesch No.1070 Made in Germany 14. COMMENTS: Kestner, circa 1914. VALUE POINTS: very beautiful example of the gentle faced baby with pleasing dewy patina of bisque, original body finish. $3000/3500

104. German Bisque Toddler, "Hilda" by Kestner

19" (48 cm). Bisque socket head, blue glass sleep eyes, painted curly lashes, short feathered brows, accented nostrils and eye corners, open mouth, outlined lips, two porcelain upper teeth, tongue, auburn mohair wig over plaster pate, composition and wooden ball-jointed toddler body with side-hip jointing, pale rose cotton toddler dress, undergarments, silk and lace bonnet. CONDITION: generally excellent. MARKS: F made in Germany 13 JDK 1914 c. Hilda Ges Gesch. COMMENTS: Kestner, circa 1914. VALUE POINTS: rarer toddler body complements the expressive yet gentle features, excellent bisque and painting. $3000/3500

105. German Paper Mache Lady with "Beehive" Coiffure

20" (51 cm). Paper mache shoulderhead of adult woman with cameo-shaped face and elongated throat, black sculpted hair arranged with elaborate beehive braids at top of head and wide pouf wings at the side, painted facial features, brown eyes, black upper eyeliner, single stroke black brows, closed mouth with delicately painted lips, original slender kid body with wooden limbs, red painted flat shoes, antique gown and undergarments. CONDITION: good, little crazing and minor touch-up on face. COMMENTS: Germany, circa 1840. VALUE POINTS: rare model with perfectly preserved elaborate coiffure. $600/800

106. Very Rare French Bisque Character Poupee by Jumeau

31" (79 cm). Bisque swivel head on kid-edged bisque shoulderplate, oval facial modelling and elongated throat portraying adult woman, large blue glass paperweight inset eyes, dark eyeliner encircles the large and expressive eyecuts, painted curly lashes, brushstroked and multi-feathered brows, shaded nostrils, closed mouth with beautifully shaped lips turned up at the corners and outlined, separately modelled pierced ears, blonde mohair wig in original ornate coiffure over cork pate, kid gusset jointed fashion body with stitched and separated fingers, silk bergere costume with wide brimmed bonnet and red leather shoes, antique basket of flowers. CONDITION: generally excellent, tiny wig pull, some body repair. MARKS: 10 Depose Tete Jumeau Bte SGDG 10. COMMENTS: Emile Jumeau, the rare model was created as a prelude to the firm's 200 character series; an identical model with different neck construction was made by Jumeau for the Roullet et Decamps automaton known as "Shepherdess" or "Bergere", circa 1889. VALUE POINTS: very rare poupee portrait from the Jumeau character series with compelling expression, fine detail of sculpting allowed by large size, and choicest bisque and painting. The bergere has her own antique French paper mache and mohair lamb with "bleating" bellows. $16,000/25,000

107. French Bisque Toddler, 236, by SFBJ in Original Trunk with Layette

14" (35 cm) doll, 21" x 11" (53 x 28 cm) trunk. A large canvas-covered wooden trunk with elaborate exterior trim opens to reveal a bisque toddler doll its elaborate costumes and accessories. The bisque socket head doll has dark glass sleep eyes, painted lower lashes, brushstroked and feathered brows, accented eye corners and nostrils, closed mouth with shaded and accented lips, two porcelain upper teeth, blonde mohair wig, French composition and wooden ball-jointed toddler body with side-hip jointing. CONDITION: generally excellent. MARKS: SFBJ 236 Paris 6 (head) (also original SFBJ paper label on torso). COMMENTS: SFBJ, circa 1917. VALUE POINTS: in unplayed with condition, the expressive-faced toddler is presented in her original trunk having two drawers filled with original costumes, toiletries and accessories. $2200/2800

108. German All-Bisque Mignonette for Au Nain Bleu

7" (18 cm). Bisque swivel head on kid-edged bisque torso, blue glass sleep eyes, painted lashes, feathered brows, accented nostrils, closed mouth with center accent line, blonde mohair wig, peg-jointed bisque arms and legs, painted black stockings to above the knees, black one strap shoes. CONDITION: generally excellent. COMMENTS: Simon and Halbig, circa 1895. VALUE POINTS: the black-stockinged girl wears her original green silk dress and matching bonnet, muslin undergarments with original silk label from the Parisian doll shop of "Au Nain Bleu", and is preserved in her original box with gilt lettering "bebe". $800/1100

108A. Petite French Bisque Bebe "Depose Jumeau"

12" (30 cm). Bisque socket head, amber brown glass paperweight inset eyes with spiral threading, painted lashes, brushstroked brows, accented nostrils and eye corners, closed mouth with defined space between the outlined lips, pierced ears, blonde mohair wig over cork pate, French composition and wooden fully jointed body with straight wrists, nicely costumed in magenta silk and lace, undergarments, Jumeau stockings, antique leather shoes. CONDITION: generally excellent. MARKS: Depose Jumeau 3 (head, and artist checkmarks) Jumeau Medaille d'Or Paris (body). COMMENTS: Emile Jumeau, circa 1885. VALUE POINTS: most appealing petite size with original wig, body, body finish, choicest bisque. $3200/2800

109. French Bisque Bebe Jumeau in Rose Silk Costume

19" (48 cm). Bisque socket head, large brown glass paperweight inset eyes, painted lashes, brushstroked and feathered brows, hint of rose blushed eyeshadow, accented nostrils, closed mouth with accented lips, pierced ears, brunette mohair wig over cork pate, French composition and wooden fully jointed body, costumed in elaborate rose silk and lace dress, matching bonnet, antique undergarments and white leather shoes with silver buckles. CONDITION: faint early hairline at right temple. MARKS: Depose Tete Jumeau Bte SGDG 8 (head, and artist checkmarks). Jumeau Medaille d'Or Paris (body). COMMENTS: Emile Jumeau, circa 1890. VALUE POINTS: pretty creamy complexioned bisque is appealing contrast to large brown paperweight eyes, original body and body finish. The doll was shown in Seeley's *Judging Dolls* and *Doll Costuming* books. $3000/3500

110. Rare French Bisque Bebe by Joanny

23" (58 cm). Bisque socket head modelled with full lower cheeks and smaller eyecuts lending a character-like expression, blue glass paperweight inset eyes, painted lashes with "dot" highlights, rose blushed eyeshadow, brushstroked and multi-feathered brows, accented eye corners, shaded nostrils, closed mouth with defined space between the artfully outlined lips, pierced ears, brunette mohair wig over cork pate, French composition and wooden fully jointed body, antique muslin print dress, undergarments, straw bonnet, silk shoes. CONDITION: generally excellent, body not original but appropriately styled and sized and of the era. MARKS: J-10 (incised). COMMENTS: attributed to Joseph Louis Joanny, circa 1885. The firm was located at 202 rue de Rivoli, Paris, from 1884-1898. Few bebes by this firm were made. VALUE POINTS: especially fine quality of creamy bisque and artful painting on the rare bebe with fine attention to detail of eyeshadow and lips. $4500/6500

111. French Bisque Bebe Jumeau in Fine Antique Costume

25" (63 cm). Bisque socket head, large blue glass paperweight inset eyes, dark painted lashes, brushstroked and multi-feathered brows, accented eye corners and nostrils, closed mouth with richly shaded lips, pierced ears, brunette human hair over cork pate, French composition and wooden fully jointed body with straight wrists. CONDITION: generally excellent. MARKS: Depose Tete Jumeau 12 (head, and artist checkmarks) Jumeau Medaille d'Or Paris (body). COMMENTS: Emile Jumeau, circa 1888. VALUE POINTS: very beautiful bisque and painting, antique dress of pont d'esprit with silk banners, lace trim, undergarments, velvet bonnet, leather shoes with silver medallions.
$4000/5000

112. Very Rare German Bisque Character, 531, by Bahr and Proschild

19" (48 cm) Solid domed bisque socket head with painted boyish hair (under blonde mohair wig), painted facial features with deeply sculpted eyesockets, painted brown eyes with shaded irises, white eyedots, black and red upper eyeliner, short feathered brows, accented nostrils of upturned nose, closed mouth with defined space between the expressive outlined lips, impressed cheek dimples, composition and wooden ball-jointed body, antique mariner suit. CONDITION: generally excellent, tiny paint rub on left cheek. MARKS: 531 10. COMMENTS: Bahr and Proschild, circa 1912. VALUE POINTS: rare model with expressive pensive features, especially fine modelling around eyes, cheeks and mouth. $3000/3800

113. German All Bisque Googly

6" (15 cm). One piece bisque head and torso, brown glass sleep and side-glancing googly eyes, very long painted curly lashes, one stroke brows, pug nose with accented nostrils, closed mouth in thin-line impish smile, brunette mohair wig, loop-jointed bisque arms and legs in chubby toddler modelling, painted white socks and brown one strap shoes, antique blue and white checkered romper suit. CONDITION: generally excellent. MARKS: 111 3 Germany (head) 110 3 (inside limbs). COMMENTS: circa 1915. VALUE POINTS: most appealing impish expression on the rarely found googly. $600/800

114. German Bisque Jubilee Googly, 165, by Hertel and Schwab

11" (28 cm). Bisque socket head with rounded facial modelling, round glass sleep and side-glancing googly eyes, very long painted curly lashes, one stroke brows, accented eye corners and nostrils, button nose, closed mouth with "watermelon slice" modelling, shaded lips, blonde mohair wig, composition and wooden ball-jointed toddler body with side-hip jointing, extremely chubby torso, antique sailor costume and cap labelled "Marine". CONDITION: generally excellent, fingers broken on left hand. MARKS: 165-1. COMMENTS: Hertel and Schwab, the model they marketed as "Jubilee" googly, circa 1914. VALUE POINTS: most appealing doll with impish expression, rare chubby body style. $3000/3500

115. Rare German Bisque Character, 1286, by Franz Schmidt

14" (35 cm). Solid domed bisque socket head with deeply sculpted hair arranged in side-parted bob, a forelock curl swept across the forehead, painted facial features, blue side-glancing eyes with unique decorative glaze on eye-whites, black upper eyeliner, delicately feathered brows, rounded nose with breathing nostrils, open mouth in laughing expression with shaded lips, two sculpted upper teeth, very plump composition and wooden ball-jointed toddler body with side-hip jointing, antique costume is included. CONDITION: generally excellent, some body finish wear at upper torso. MARKS: F.S. & Co 1286/35 Made in Germany. COMMENTS: Franz Schmidt, circa 1915. VALUE POINTS: rare model with uniquely modelled hair, eye decoration, expressive features, wonderful original chubby toddler body with original finish. $3500/4500

116. German Bisque Character Known as Tommy Tucker

19" (48 cm). Solid domed bisque socket head, brown painted boyish hair with side-swept forelock curl, brown glass eyes, painted long curly lashes, short feathered brows, well-modelled larger ears, accented nostrils and eye corners, open mouth, shaded and accented lips, two porcelain upper teeth, tongue, composition bent limb baby body, antique cotton romper suit. CONDITION: generally excellent, tiny flake hidden at base of neck socket. MARKS: 13. COMMENTS: attributed to Bruno Schmidt, circa 1912. VALUE POINTS: fine quality of bisque and painting, beautifully defined hair, original body and body finish. $1100/1500

117. German All Bisque Googly, Model 293

6" (15 cm). Bisque swivel head on kid-edged bisque torso, rounded facial modelling, large blue glass side-glancing googly eyes, painted lashes, single stroke brows, closed mouth with defined space between the lips, blonde mohair wig, loop-jointed bisque arms and legs, painted blue socks and brown one-strap shoes, pretty lace dress with rose silk ribbons. CONDITION: generally excellent. MARKS: 293 14 (head and inside legs). COMMENTS: circa 1915. VALUE POINTS: most appealing googly with very expressive features, excellent bisque. $500/700

118. German Bisque Googly, Model 292

6" (15 cm). Bisque socket head, brown glass side-glancing googly eyes, long painted curly lashes, single stroke brows, pug nose, closed mouth with impish smile, brunette mohair wig, composition bent limb baby body, antique knit costume with pink bow and slippers. CONDITION: generally excellent. MARKS: 292 14. COMMENTS: circa 1915. VALUE POINTS: impish expression is wonderfully executed on the brown-eyed googly. $400/500

119. German All-Bisque Googly, Model 292

4 1/2" (11 cm). Bisque swivel head on kid-edged bisque torso, blue glass side-glancing googly eyes, painted lashes, single stroke brows, closed mouth with impish smile, brunette mohair wig, loop-jointed bisque arms and legs with blue painted socks and black one strap shoes, antique crocheted costume. CONDITION: generally excellent. MARKS: 292 10 (head and body parts). COMMENTS: circa 1915. VALUE POINTS: mischievous expression is well-rendered on the tiny googly. $300/400

120. German Bisque Toddler, 604, by Bahr and Proschild

11" (28 cm). Bisque socket head with rounded facial modelling, blue glass sleep eyes, painted curly lashes, short feathered brows, accented eye corners and nostrils, closed mouth with modelled teeth between the outlined lips, brunette mohair wig, composition body with one piece curved baby arms, toddler ball-jointed legs with side-hip jointing, pretty white woolen baby dress with ruffled bonnet, slippers, undergarments. CONDITION: generally excellent. MARKS: 604 0. COMMENTS: Bahr and Proschild, circa 1912. VALUE POINTS: dreamy-faced toddler character with very choice bisque and painting, original body and body finish. $600/800

121. German Bisque Character, 550, by Marseille

17" (43 cm). Bisque socket head, blue glass sleep eyes, painted long curly lashes, incised eyeliner, short feathered brows, accented eye corners and nostrils, closed mouth with accent line between the smiling lips, blonde mohair wig, composition and wooden ball-jointed body. CONDITION: generally excellent. MARKS: Germany 550 A 4 M DRGM. COMMENTS: Marseille, circa 1915. VALUE POINTS: rare character with superb characterization, gentle smile enhanced by impressed dimples, choice bisque, original wig, body, body finish, original antique costume, undergarments, shoes, bonnet. $1100/1500

122. Earliest Model French Bisque Bebe "Brevete" by Leon Casimir Bru

12" (30 cm). Pressed bisque swivel head on kid-edged bisque shoulderplate, amber brown glass paperweight inset eyes, dark eyeliner encircles the eyecut, painted lashes, feathered brows, accented eye corners and nostrils, closed mouth with heart-shaped upper lip, accented detail of delicate lip coloring, pierced ears, blonde lambswool wig over cork pate, original kid bebe body based on the Bru deposed model, square cut collarette, one piece curved kid upper arms with bisque hands, separately sculpted fingers, defined knuckles and nails, gusset-jointed hips and knees. CONDITION: generally excellent, left baby finger tip restored. MARKS: 3/0 (head) Bebe Brevete SGDG Paris (paper label on torso). COMMENTS: Leon Casimir Bru, circa 1879, the first model of his bebe. VALUE POINTS: very beautiful petite bebe is preserved in remarkable condition, with original very sturdy body with original label, finest quality bisque and painting. $8000/12,000

123. French Bisque Bebe Bru, Size 2, by Leon Casimir Bru

13" (33 cm). Bisque swivel head on kid-edged bisque shoulderplate with modelled bosom and shoulderblades, blue glass enamel inset eyes with spiral threading, dark eyeliner encircles the eyecut, painted lashes, feathered brows, accented eye corners and nostrils, closed mouth with very full sensuous lips, heart-shaped upper lip, modelled space between the outlined lips, pierced ears, blonde mohair wig over cork pate, French kid body with gusset-jointed hips and knees, scalloped edge kid collarette, kid-over-metal upper arms, bisque forearms, separately sculpted fingers, defined knuckles and nails. CONDITION: generally excellent. MARKS: Bru Jne 2 (head) (original Bru paper label on torso). COMMENTS: Leon Casimir Bru, circa 1884. VALUE POINTS: outstanding beauty of the petite bebe with spectacular eyes, original body in sturdy condition, perfect bisque hands, lovely antique costume includes original leather shoes signed "Bru Jne Paris 2". $12,000/16,000

124. German Bisque Child, 1279, by Simon and Halbig

24" (61 cm). Bisque socket head, dark blue glass sleep eyes, dark painted curly lashes, incised eyeliner, short feathered brows in upward slant with slight modelling detail, accented nostrils, open mouth with pale outlined lips and accent dot in center of bottom lips, four porcelain teeth, impressed cheek and chin dimples, pierced ears, blonde mohair wig, composition and wooden ball-jointed body. CONDITION: generally excellent. MARKS: S&H 1279 dep Germany 12. COMMENTS: Simon and Halbig, circa 1912. VALUE POINTS: rare model with well defined unique features including eyebrow styling, bottom lip accent dot, and impressed dimples, all enhanced by choicest modelling and bisque, original body and body finish, antique dress, undergarments, leather boots. $2500/3000

125. German Bisque Character "Dolly Dimple" by Gebruder Heubach

21" (53 cm). Bisque socket head, very large brown glass sleep eyes, dark eyeliner encircles the eyecuts, short dark painted lashes, incised eyeliner, delicately fringed brows, accented eye corners and nostrils, open mouth in smiling expression with outlined lips, four modelled upper teeth, impressed dimples around the mouth, blonde mohair wig, composition and wooden ball-jointed body, antique dress, undergarments, lace and silk bonnet, stockings, black leather shoes. CONDITION: generally excellent. MARKS: 9. COMMENTS: Gebruder Heubach, the doll is identical to their model "Dolly Dimple" made for Hamburger and Co, circa 1910. VALUE POINTS: very beautiful wide-eyed child has flawless bisque with outstanding modelling, original body and body finish, antique wig and costume. $2000/2500

> **There are certain dolls that, even after 40 years of living with me, still give a jolt of happiness every time I pass them.**
>
> Mildred Seeley in
> *For the Love of Dolls and Roses*

126. Large German Bisque Pouty, 115A, by Kammer and Reinhardt

28" (68 cm). Bisque socket head, brilliant blue glass paperweight inset eyes, dark eyeliner encircles the eyecut, dark painted curly lashes, brushstroked and feathered brows, accented nostrils and eye corners, closed mouth in pouty expression, shaded and accented lips, (new) long blonde human hair wig, composition and wooden ball-jointed toddler body with side-hip jointing, antique white dress, undergarments, leather shoes. CONDITION: generally excellent, eyes are atypical for this model. MARKS: K*R S&H 115/A 68. COMMENTS: Kammer and Reinhardt, their model marketed as Phillip, circa 1912. Value Points: exceptional quality of sculpting on this large 115A model is enhanced by very beautiful eyes, superb painting and complexion, original rare toddler body with original finish. A favorite doll of Seeley, the doll appeared in many of her books. $4500/6500

127. Very Rare German Bisque "Wunderkind" Characters by Kestner

15" (38 cm). A red cardboard box with four compartments contains within its original bisque doll and three additional interchangeable heads. The doll has bisque socket head, brown glass sleep eyes, painted lashes, brushstroked brows with decorative glaze, accented nostrils, open mouth, shaded and accented lips, four porcelain teeth, brunette mohair wig over plaster pate, composition and wooden ball-jointed body. Each of the three additional heads have painted eyes and facial features, closed mouths with different expressions, original mohair wigs over plaster pates. CONDITION: generally excellent. MARKS: B made in Germany 6 171 10 (head) Germany (body). 183 (blue eyed girl with four teeth). 179 (blue eyed boy with modelled space between lips). 182 (brown-eyed pouty girl). COMMENTS: Kestner, circa 1910, the multi-head character series was marketed as "das Wunderkind". VALUE POINTS: in pristine unplayed with condition, the rare dolls are presented in original box with amusing illustration of the dolls on the cover. $9000/14,000

128. German Bisque Child, 949, by Simon and Halbig

13" (33 cm). Bisque socket head, brown glass sleep eyes, painted lashes, brushstroked brows, accented nostrils and eye corners, open mouth with accented lips, two square cut upper teeth, one square cut lower tooth, pierced ears, blonde mohair wig, Sonneberg composition and wooden ball-jointed body with straight wrists and loose ball joints at hips, nice antique costume. CONDITION: generally excellent. MARKS: SH 5 949. COMMENTS: Simon and Halbig, circa 1885. VALUE POINTS: very pretty shy-faced expression with slightly parted lips and square cut teeth, pleasing bisque and painting. $1100/1400

129. German Bisque Character, 185, by Kestner

11" (28 cm). Bisque socket head, blue glass sleep eyes, painted lashes, short feathered brows, accented nostrils, closed mouth with smiling expression, accented lips, row of painted teeth, brunette mohair braids, composition and wooden ball-jointed body. CONDITION: generally excellent. MARKS: 185. COMMENTS: Kestner, the glass-eyed version of their 183 model, circa 1912. VALUE POINTS: most appealing little character with choice modelling and painting, original wig, body, body finish, antique costume and original shoes. $2200/2800

131. German Bisque Pouty, 115/A, by Kammer and Reinhardt

15" (38 cm). Bisque socket head, blue glass sleep eyes, painted curly lashes, short brushstroked brows, accented nostrils, closed mouth with pouty expression, shaded lips with decorative glaze, auburn human hair, five piece composition toddler body with side-hip jointing nicely costumed. CONDITION: small flake on upper right eye rim, one finger tip chipped. MARKS: K*R Simon & Halbig 115/A 38. COMMENTS: Kammer and Reinhardt, circa 1912, their model marketed as "Phillip". VALUE POINTS: especially fine quality of bisque with dewy patina complexion enhances the pouty expression. $2200/2800

132. German Bisque Character, 1295, by Franz Schmidt

9" (23 cm). Bisque socket head, brown glass sleep eyes, very long curly lashes, short feathered brows, accented eye corners and nostrils, open mouth with richly shaded lips, brunette mohair wig, composition five piece toddler body with side-hip jointing and very chubby stomach, antique costume. CONDITION: generally excellent, some faint pulls under the wig. MARKS: 1295 F. S. & Co. made in Germany 23. COMMENTS: Franz Schmidt, circa 1920. VALUE POINTS: appealing wide-eyed character with well-modelled toddler body. $400/500

133. German Brown-Complexioned Bisque Character, "Marie", by Kammer and Reinhardt

12" (30 cm). Bisque socket head with brown complexion, painted brown eyes with heavily modelled eyelids, black upper eyeliner, single stroke tapered brows, closed mouth with very full coral lips, brunette mohair fleecy wig, brown composition and wooden ball-

130. German Bisque Toddler, 126, by Kammer and Reinhardt

10" (25 cm). Bisque socket head, brown glass sleep eyes, painted lashes, feathered brows, accented nostrils, open mouth, accented lips, two porcelain upper teeth, brunette human hair, composition five piece toddler body with side-hip jointing and chubby torso, nicely costumed, antique shoes. CONDITION: generally excellent. MARKS: K*R Simon & Halbig 126 Germany 23. COMMENTS: Kammer and Reinhardt, circa 1920. VALUE POINTS: wide-eyed toddler has excellent bisque and painting, original body and body finish. $500/700

jointed body. CONDITION: generally excellent, some typical wig pulls at back of head. MARKS: K*R 101 30. COMMENTS: Kammer and Reinhardt, circa 1910, the model of their character series marketed as "Marie". VALUE POINTS: rarer brown-complexioned "Marie" has very pleasing complexion and beautifully painted lips and eyes, antique costume. $2000/2500

134. German Bisque Character, "Hans", by Kammer and Reinhardt
13" (32 cm). Bisque socket head, painted facial features of wistful faced boy, blue eyes, black upper eyeliner, short stroke brows, accented nostrils, closed mouth with center accent line, brunette mohair wig, composition and wooden ball-jointed body, nicely costumed as young schoolboy with brass horn and silver whistle. CONDITION: generally excellent, some typical wig pulls. MARKS: K*R 114 30. COMMENTS: Kammer and Reinhardt, circa 1910, their model marketed as "Hans". VALUE POINTS: pouty faced character boy has well modelled features for this smaller example. $1600/1900

135. French Bisque Lady Doll by Emile Jumeau

24" (61 cm). Bisque socket head, large blue glass paperweight inset eyes, dark eyeliner encircles the eyecut, painted dark curly lashes, incised eyeliner, arched feathered brows, accented eye corners, shaded nostrils, closed mouth with shaded and outlined lips, defined space between the lips, upturned lip corners, pierced ears, brunette mohair wig in upswept coiffure, French composition and wooden body with adult female shaping, defined bosom, tiny waist, accentuated derriere, slightly elongated limbs. CONDITION: generally excellent. MARKS: Depose Tete Jumeau Bte SGDG 10 (head, and artist checkmarks) Bebe Jumeau Diplome d'Honneur (body). COMMENTS: Emile Jumeau, circa 1892. VALUE POINTS: choice bisque and painting, rarer lady body is enhanced by costume of aqua green and black lace, net stockings, with antique black elbow-length fingerless gloves, black leather shoes. $6000/7500

136. Outstanding French Bisque Bebe by Schmitt et Fils

31" (79 cm). Pressed bisque socket head with pear-shaped facial modelling, very full cheeks, almond shaped brown glass inset eyes with spiral threading, dark eyeliner encircles the eyecuts, painted dark lashes, mauve blushed eyeshadow, brushstroked and multi-feathered brows, accented eye corners, shaded nostrils, closed mouth with defined space between the shaded and outlined lips, heart-shaped upper and lower lips, dimpled blushed chin, pierced blushed ears, blonde mohair wig, French composition and wooden eight-loose-ball-jointed body with flat-cut derriere, curled fingers, shapely definition of ankles and feet. CONDITION: generally excellent. MARKS: 8 Sch (shield mark on head and flat cut of derriere). COMMENTS: Schmitt et Fils, circa 1884. VALUE POINTS: outstanding beauty and quality of the large bebe, choicest bisque and modelling, rich brown eyes enhancing the artistic painting, original body and body finish; the doll wears antique undergarments and an elaborate gown of teal and ivory silk satin, along with matching bonnet, antique shoes, gloves and beaded purse. A particular favorite of Mildred Seeley, the doll was featured in many of her books. $17,000/23,000

137. French Brown-Complexioned Bisque Bebe by Steiner
11" (28 cm). Chocolate brown bisque socket head, brown glass inset eyes, painted black lashes, black brushstroked and feathered brows, accented nostrils, open mouth, shaded lips, row of porcelain teeth, pierced ears, black mohair wig over cork pate, French brown composition and wooden fully-jointed body, nicely costumed in French-style dress, undergarments, black stockings, brown shoes. CONDITION: generally excellent. MARKS: A 1. COMMENTS: Jules Steiner, circa 1890. VALUE POINTS: very pleasing brown complexion with enhancing dewy patina on the bright-eyed bebe in appealing petite size. $1700/2200

138. French Bisque Bebe, Figure B, with Wire-Lever Sleep Eyes by Jules Steiner
18" (46 cm). Bisque socket head, dark blue glass sleep eyes that operate from lever at back of head, painted lashes with "dot" highlights, rose blushed eyeshadow, thickly fringed brows with feathered highlights, accented eye corners, shaded nostrils, open mouth with slightly parted outlined lips, double row of tiny porcelain teeth, pierced ears, auburn mohair wig, French composition and wooden fully jointed body, wearing mauve taffeta dress with lace trim; the undergarments, bonnet and shoes are antique. CONDITION: generally excellent, arms are French and appropriately sized although not original to body. MARKS: J. Steiner Bte SGDG Paris Fre B 11 (head) Le Petit Parisien Bebe Steiner (torso stamp) (eyes also signed J. Steiner). COMMENTS: Jules Steiner, circa 1885. VALUE POINTS: the rarer model, Figure B, with wonderful painting of brows and shadow, choice bisque, rarer lever sleep eyes. $3800/4500

139. Rare Petite Early Bebe Steiner from Au Nain Bleu

10" (25 cm). Bisque socket head with rounded facial modelling, blue glass enamel inset eyes with spiral threading, painted lashes, arched delicately feathered brows, accented nostrils and eye corners, closed mouth with accented pale lips, pierced ears, blonde lambswool wig, unusual composition and wooden fully jointed body with loose ball-joints at elbows and knees and classic Steiner separated fingers, included is maroon silk dress and bonnet, shoes and socks. CONDITION: generally excellent. MARKS: 3/0. COMMENTS: Jules Steiner, circa 1880. VALUE POINTS: rare and very appealing petite bebe with distinctive and original body, wears original muslin chemise and pantalets, has original paper label on body from the Paris doll shop of Au Nain Bleu. $3000/4000

140. French Bisque Bebe, Series C, by Jules Steiner

14" (35 cm). Bisque socket head with rounded facial modelling, blue glass sleep eyes that operate from lever at back of head, painted lashes with "dot" highlights, rose blushed eyeshadow, fringed brows with feathered detail, accented nostrils and eye corners, closed mouth with accented lips, pierced ears, blonde lambswool wig over Steiner pate, French composition fully jointed body with straight wrists, nicely costumed in white cotton gown with embroidered detail, undergarments, lace cap, shoes and stockings. CONDITION: generally excellent, tiny flake at right pierced ear hole. MARKS: Sie C o (incised) J. Steiner Bte SGDG, Bourgoin (tiny pencil script) (Steiner caduceus stamp on torso)(eyes also signed J. Steiner). COMMENTS: J. Steiner, circa 1882. VALUE POINTS: beautiful early Steiner bebe with exquisite delicate painting, original body and body finish. $3500/4500

141. French Bisque Poupee Attributed to Jumeau

17" (43 cm). Bisque swivel head on kid-edged bisque shoulderplate, grey glass enamel inset eyes, dark eyeliner encircles the eyecut, painted lashes, feathered brows, accented nostrils and eye corners, closed mouth with pale accented lips, pierced ears, blonde mohair wig in elaborate coiffure on cork pate, German kid gusset-jointed body, bisque forearms, nicely costumed in lavender gown with black lace trim. CONDITION: bisque head and shoulderplate excellent, body not original but appropriately sized, right bisque hand repaired. MARKS: 4 (head and shoulderplate). COMMENTS: the bisque head attributed to Jumeau, circa 1875. VALUE POINTS: very beautiful face with artistic painting of features and complexion. $700/1100

142. French Bisque Poupee with Elaborate Head Articulation

22" (56 cm). Pale bisque swivel head with rounded facial modelling, on kid-edged shoulderplate, articulation allowing the head to tilt forward, tilt from side to side and swivel based on the Dehors deposed system, pale blue/grey enamel eyes with spiral threading and darker blue outer rims, painted lashes, feathered brows, accented eye corners and nostrils, very delicate mauve eyeshadow, closed mouth with accented and shaded lips, pierced ears, French bisque body with gusset jointed hips and knees, bisque forearms, lovely maroon silk gown, bonnet, undergarments, unusual antique green velvet heeled shoes. CONDITION: generally excellent, bisque forearms are not original. MARKS: 7 (front shoulderplate). COMMENTS: circa 1867, maker unknown. VALUE POINTS: beautiful poupee with exquisite decoration. $2500/3100

143. French Bisque Smiling Poupee by Leon Casimir Bru

20" (51 cm). Bisque swivel head on kid-edged bisque shoulderplate, almond shaped blue glass enamel inset eyes with darker blue outer rims, dark eyeliner encircles the sockets, painted short curly lashes, arched feathered brows, accented eye corners and nostrils, closed mouth with full lips posed in enigmatic smile, accent lines enhance the softly shaded lips, pierced ears, blonde mohair wig over cork pate, French kid fashion body with gusset jointing, stitched and separated fingers, nicely costumed in rose and lavender gown, straw bonnet, undergarments, shoes. CONDITION: generally excellent, the hands and wrists have been tinted rose as though to suggest gloves, other minor body patching. MARKS: G (head) H (shoulderplate). COMMENTS: Leon Casimir Bru, circa 1873 when the smiling face model was deposed by Bru; the inspiration for this model is discussed in *The Bru Book*. VALUE POINTS: very beautiful smiling poupee has choicest bisque and artistic painting, original head and shoulderplate, compelling expression. $3000/3800

144. Early French Bisque Poupee by Barrois

16" (40 cm). Pale bisque shoulderhead with rounded facial modelling, cobalt blue glass enamel inset eyes in oval shaping, dark eyeliner encircles the eyecut, painted lashes, arched feathered brows, accented nostrils, closed mouth with pale accented lips, unpierced ears, brunette mohair wig over cork pate, French kid fashion body with gusset jointing at hips, brown leather arms. CONDITION: generally excellent, arms are antique but not original to doll. MARKS: E 3 Depose B. COMMENTS: Barrois, circa 1860, the depose marking is reference to the glass inset eyes on this early model. VALUE POINTS: very beautiful pale bisque with rich contrasting eyes, very fine antique costume. $2200/2500

145. German Bisque Fashion Doll for the French Market in Original Wedding Costume

21" (53 cm). Bisque socket head, blue glass sleep eyes, mohair lashes, painted lower lashes, slightly modelled brushstroked brows with feathering, accented nostrils, open mouth, outlined lips, four porcelain teeth, pierced ears, brunette human hair in elaborate coiffure, French composition and wooden fully jointed body with shapely female modelling, modelled bosom, tiny waist, accentuated derriere. CONDITION: generally excellent. MARKS: 1159 S&H dep 8 (head) Bebe Jumeau Diplome d'Honneur (body). COMMENTS: Simon and Halbig bisque head for Jumeau/SFBJ, circa 1898. VALUE POINTS: outstanding and perfectly preserved all original fashionable bride from the end of the 19th century, wearing original ivory satin wedding gown with train, lace trim and wax orange blossoms, flower trimmed veil, undergarments include petticoat with train, white leather ankle shoes signed C.P. $2800/3500

146. German All-Bisque Miniature by Kestner

5" (13 cm). Bisque swivel head on kid-edged bisque torso, blue glass sleep eyes, painted lashes, arched feathered brows, accented nostrils, closed mouth with pertly shaped

accented lips, brunette mohair wig, peg-jointed bisque arms and legs with cupped hands, bare feet, very shapely legs. Condition: generally excellent, minor flakes at leg rims. MARKS: 0. COMMENTS: Kestner, circa 1885. VALUE POINTS: excellent attention to detail of painting and wonderfully modelled legs and hands on the early swivel head doll. $500/600

147. French Bisque Poupee in Antique Costume

15" (38 cm). Very pale bisque swivel head on kid-edged bisque shoulderplate, cobalt blue glass enamel inset eyes, very dark eyeliner encircles the eyecut, short painted lashes, slightly arched feathered brows, accented nostrils, closed mouth with pale outlined lips, ears pierced into head, blonde mohair wig over cork pate, French kid fashion body with gusset jointing at hips, kid over wooden upper arms, bisque forearms. CONDITION: generally excellent, left hand repaired. COMMENTS: circa 1868. VALUE POINTS: compelling blue eyes compliment the pale complexion, beautiful costume of magenta and purple velvet with silk and lace trim, matching bonnet with velvet pansies, taffeta skirt and reticule, undergarments, shoes. $2500/3000

148. German Paper Mache Lady Doll with Elaborate Coiffure
11" (28 cm). Paper mache shoulderhead of adult woman with cameo-shaped face and elongated throat, very elaborate sculpted coiffure with three pouf rolls at top of head above horizontal braids and wide side curls, painted turquoise eyes, black upper eyeliner, single stroke brows, closed mouth, blushed cheeks, very slender muslin body with tiny waist, wooden lower limbs, painted black ankle boots, muslin gown in 1840 style. CONDITION: some craquelure on shoulderplate, original paint throughout. COMMENTS: Germany, circa 1840. VALUE POINTS: exquisite modelling of hair, slightly modelled bosom, original finish. $500/700

149. German Paper Mache Lady Doll in Larger Size

16" (40 cm). Paper mache shoulderhead with slender oval face and elongated throat, black modelled hair in centerparted style drawn around the sides of face into two deep loops and finger curls, and into tight bun at back of head, painted turquoise eyes, black upper eyeliner, singles stroke brows, closed mouth, accented lips, blushed cheeks, very slender kid body with wooden lower limbs, painted orange flat shoes, costumed in antique fabrics of ivory silk and burgundy velvet with soutache gold braid, undergarments. CONDITION: generally excellent, some craquelure to back shoulderplate, right thumb chipped. COMMENTS: Germany, circa 1850. VALUE POINTS: serene expression is well preserved, unusual coiffure, original body. $500/700

150. German Paper Mache Child Doll

9" (23 cm). Paper mache shoulderhead with rounded childlike modelling, short black sculpted curly hair, painted large dark blue eyes, black upper eyeliner, single stroke brows, closed mouth, very slender kid body with wooden limbs, painted yellow shoes, maroon gown and undergarments. CONDITION: some retouch to hair. COMMENTS: Germany, circa 1860. VALUE POINTS: appealing petite size has original body. $300/400

151. Very Petite German Paper Mache Child Doll

7" (18 cm). Paper mache shoulderhead with black sculpted hair drawn smoothly around the face into uniform finger curls, painted facial features, very large dark blue eyes, black upper eyeliner, single stroke brows, closed mouth, very slender kid body, wooden lower arms and legs, painted yellow boots. CONDITION: very good. COMMENTS: Germany, circa 1860. VALUE POINTS: the petite doll is in original condition with original painting, wearing possibly original bronze green silk dress and apron, undergarments. $400/500

152. French Bisque Poupee by Leon Casimir Bru with Depose Wooden Body

16" (40 cm). Bisque swivel head on kid-edged bisque shoulderplate, blue glass enamel inset eyes, painted lashes with heavily modelled eyelids, dark upper eyeliner, arched feathered brows, accented nostrils and eye corners, closed mouth with pale accented lips, ears pierced into the head, blonde human hair over cork pate, all wooden body with dowel-jointing at shoulders, elbows, wrists, hips, knees and ankles, separately carved fingers and toes, defined nails, ball-swivel waist, scalloped-edge kid collarette, green bronze silk gown and undergarments included. CONDITION: generally excellent, some paint wear on original body finish. MARKS: F. COMMENTS: Leon Casimir Bru, circa 1869, based on the Bru wooden-body patent of that date, this being the first facial model used for that body. VALUE POINTS: beautiful early letter series Bru poupee with original wooden body. $3500/4500

107

153. French Bisque Bebe by Jumeau

17" (43 cm). Bisque socket head, blue glass paperweight inset eyes, very lushly painted long lashes, brushstroked and multi-feathered brows, accented nostrils and eye corners, closed mouth with outlined very full lips, pierced ears, French composition and wooden fully jointed body, green silk dress and bonnet, white leather slippers, undergarments. CONDITION: generally excellent. MARKS: 9 (and artist checkmarks on head) Bebe Jumeau Diplome d'Honneur (body). COMMENTS: Jumeau, circa 1890. VALUE POINTS: an unusual facial model with very expressive features, artistic painting. $3000/3800

154. German All-Bisque Mignonette with Bare Feet

5" (13 cm). Bisque swivel head on kid-edged bisque torso, cobalt blue glass inset eyes, painted lashes, single stroke brows, accented nostrils, closed mouth with center accent line, brunette mohair wig peg-jointed bisque arms and legs, modelled bent elbows, shapely legs with bare feet, antique white embroidered dress and lace cap. CONDITION: generally excellent. MARKS: 8. COMMENTS: circa 1880. VALUE POINTS: rarity factors include swivel head, cobalt eyes, bare feet, closed mouth. $500/700

155. German All-Bisque Mignonette by Kestner

5" (13 cm). Bisque swivel head on kid-edged bisque torso, blue glass sleep eyes, painted lashes, feathered brows, accented nostrils, closed mouth, blonde mohair wig over plaster pate, peg-jointed bisque arms and legs, cupped hands, shapely legs with bare feet, antique costume. CONDITION: generally excellent. MARKS: 0. COMMENTS: Kestner, circa 1885. VALUE POINTS: most appealing little doll with very choice bisque and painting, rarer bare feet and swivel head. $600/900

156. French Bisque Bebe Known as "Circle/Dot" by Leon Casimir Bru

12" (30 cm). Bisque swivel head on kid-edged bisque shoulderplate with modelled bosom and shoulderblades, brown glass inset eyes with defined spiral threading, painted lashes, incised eyeliner, brushstroked and multi-feathered brows, accented nostrils, closed mouth with defined space between the shaded and outlined lips, pierced ears, blonde mohair wig over cork pate, French kid bebe body with gusset jointing of hips and knees, curved kid upper arms, bisque forearms with separately sculpted fingers, antique rose cotton and lace costume, silk bonnet, undergarments, rose net stockings, antique rose kid shoes. CONDITION: generally excellent, seam line

firing flaw below right ear. MARKS: (circle/dot symbol). COMMENTS: Leon Casimir Bru, circa 1880. VALUE POINTS: the petite bebe has original sturdy body, very fine definition of facial modelling and painting, perfect bisque hands. $7000/9000

157. French Bisque Bebe by Leon Casimir Bru

18" (46 cm). Bisque swivel head on kid-edged bisque shoulderplate with modelled bosom and shoulderblades, deep blue glass enamel inset eyes with spiral threading, painted lashes, incised eyeliner, rose blushed eyeshadow, brushstroked and feathered brows, accented eye corners, shaded nostrils, closed mouth with space between the outlined lips, heart-shaped upper lip, pierced ears, dimpled chin, blonde mohair wig over cork pate, French kid body with gusset jointed hips and knees, kid over wooden upper arms, bisque forearms with separately sculpted fingers, defined knuckles and nails, beautiful Bru style jacket dress, silk bonnet, undergarments, antique leather shoes. CONDITION: generally excellent. MARKS: Bru Jne 8 (head) Bru Jne (left shoulder) No.6 (right shoulder). COMMENTS: Leon Casimir Bru, circa 1884. VALUE POINTS: the luminous blue eyes enhance the deeply modelled facial features, body especially sturdy with perfect bisque hands. $11,000/14,000

158. Rare French Bisque Transitional Model Bebe Bru Jne

17" (43 cm). Pressed bisque socket head, blue glass paperweight inset eyes with prominent spiral threading, dark eyeliner encircles the eyecut, painted lashes, mauve blushed eyeshadow, brushstroked and multi-feathered brows, accented eye corners, shaded nostrils, pierced ears, blonde lambswool wig over cork pate, French gusset-jointed kid bebe body with curved kid upper arms, bisque forearms with sculpted fingers, defined knuckles and nails, green silk print dress with lace trim, undergarments, green net stockings and brown leather shoes. CONDITION: generally excellent. MARKS: Bru Jne 5 (head) Bru Jne (left shoulderplate) No. 5 (right shoulderplate). COMMENTS: Leon Casimir Bru, circa 1882, a rare transitional model that retains the look of the earlier Brevete bebe but with Bru Jne signature. VALUE POINTS: gorgeous Bru bebe with exemplary bisque and painting, very sturdy original early kid body with perfect bisque hands. $12,000/17,000

159. German All Bisque Doll by Kestner with Yellow Boots

10" (25 cm). Bisque swivel head on kid-edged bisque torso, brown glass enamel inset eyes, painted lashes, single stroke brows, accented nostrils, closed mouth with modelled space between the outlined lips, pierced ears, peg-jointed bisque arms and legs, cupped fingers, very muscular legs with dimpled knees, shapely ankles, painted white ribbed stockings, yellow ankle boots with black spats and heels, green silk dress included. CONDITION: generally excellent, minor flakes at peg holes. COMMENTS: Kestner, circa 1882, the model is referred to as "French Wrestler" in reference to its muscular body. VALUE POINTS: rare and large model with beautifully defined body features. $800/1100

160. German All-Bisque Doll by Kestner with Blue Boots

6" (15 cm). Bisque swivel head on kid-edged bisque torso, brown glass inset eyes, painted lashes, brushstroked brows, accented nostrils and eye corners, closed mouth with accent line between the lips, brunette mohair ringlet curled wig, peg-jointed bisque arms and legs, painted white stockings with lavender ties, blue ankle boots. CONDITION: generally excellent, tiny pinflakes on peg holes. MARKS: 0. COMMENTS: Kestner, circa 1885. VALUE POINTS: the petite all bisque has very beautiful face and painting, highly defined body features and painting. $600/800

161. French Bisque Mechanical Walking Bebe by Bru

24" (61 cm). Pressed bisque socket head, deep blue glass paperweight inset eyes, dark eyeliner encircles the eyecuts, painted lashes, mauve blushed eyeshadow, arched multi-feathered brows, accented eye corners and nostrils, closed mouth with shaded and accented lips, pierced ears, blonde mohair wig over cork pate, French composition and wooden body with jointing at shoulders, elbows and wrists, one piece legs with attached metal-based wheeled feet. A clockwork mechanism, contained in the torso, causes the doll to "walk" when turned; the doll slowly lifts each foot in turn. CONDITION: generally excellent, mechanism functions well, bisque head is Bru Brevete model on later mechanical walking body. COMMENTS: Bru, the Brevete model head, circa 1882. VALUE POINTS: very beautiful bebe face with softest blush complexion, luminous eyes, well-functioning mechanical walking device, antique costume. $7000/9000

162. German Bisque Pouty, 7672, by Gebruder Heubach

14" (35 cm). Solid domed bisque socket head, blonde painted boyish hair, blue intaglio eyes with white eyedots, accented nostrils and eye corners, closed mouth with downcast lips, composition and wooden ball-jointed body, nicely costumed. CONDITION: generally excellent, some body touch-up. MARKS: 4 Germany Heubach (sunburst mark) 7672 dep. COMMENTS: Gebruder Heubach, circa 1915. VALUE POINTS: fine modelling and bisque on the wistful faced character. $400/500

163. German All Bisque Character Boy by Gebruder Heubach

8" (20 cm). One piece bisque head and torso, modelled short brown boyish hair with side-swept forelock curls, brown side-glancing eyes, painted upper lashes, short feathered brows, accented nostrils and eye corners, closed mouth with impish smile, accented lips, loop-jointed bisque arms and legs, starfish-style modelled fingers, painted white socks and brown buckled shoes, costumed. CONDITION: generally excellent. MARKS: 10511.3. COMMENTS: Gebruder Heubach, circa 1918. VALUE POINTS: wonderful detail of sculpting expression on face, well detailed body with blushed enhancement. $600/900

164. German Bisque Laughing Character, 7364, by Heubach

12" (30 cm). Solid domed bisque socket head, brown painted boyish hair with combmarked detail, blue intaglio side-glancing eyes with large black pupils, white eyedots, black and incised upper eyeliner, accented nostrils and eye corners, closed mouth in laughing expression with shaded lips, two beaded lower teeth, composition five piece toddler body, nicely costumed. CONDITION: generally excellent. MARKS: Heubach (in square) 4 7364 Germany. COMMENTS: Gebruder Heubach, circa 1917. VALUE POINTS: very expressive model enhanced by laughter crinkles around the eyes and mouth, impressed cheek dimples, original body finish. $500/700

165. German All Bisque Character Girl by Gebruder Heubach

8" (20 cm). One piece bisque head and torso, sculpted short brown curly hair with blue hairbow, side-glancing brown eyes with enhancing decorative glaze, short feathered brows, accented nostrils, closed mouth with impish smile, loop-jointed bisque arms and legs with toddler modelling, painted white socks with brown shoes decorated with bows, pretty costume. CONDITION: generally excellent. MARKS: 10499. COMMENTS: Gebruder Heubach, circa 1918. VALUE POINTS : appealing shy-faced little girl with excellent bisque and painting. $600/900

166. German Bisque Character, "Peter", by Kammer and Reinhardt

11" (26 cm). Bisque socket head, blue painted eyes, black upper eyeliner, single stroke tapered brows, accented nostrils, closed mouth with pouty expression, blonde mohair wig, composition and wooden ball-jointed body, nicely costumed in blue knit wear. CONDITION: generally excellent, few wig pulls. MARKS: K*R 101 26. COMMENTS: Kammer and Reinhardt, their model "Peter" from their art character reform series, circa 1910. VALUE POINTS: appealing size of the wistful child, original body, body finish and wig. $1400/1800

167. German Bisque Character, "Marie" by Kammer and Reinhardt

18" (46 cm). Bisque socket head, painted facial features, dark blue eyes with tiny black pupils, heavily modelled eyelids, black upper eyeliner, one stroke tapered brows, accented nostrils, closed mouth with full pouty lips, accented lips, blonde mohair wig, composition and wooden ball-jointed body, antique costume. CONDITION: generally excellent. MARKS: K*R 101 46. COMMENTS: Kammer and Reinhardt, circa 1910, from their art character series. VALUE POINTS: very beautiful modelling with highly defined features, choice painting and bisque, original body finish. $3000/3500

168. French Bisque Bebe Teteur by Leon Casimir Bru

13" (33 cm). Bisque swivel head on kid-edged bisque shoulderplate, blue glass paperweight inset eyes, painted curly lashes, fringed brows, accented nostrils and eye corners, open mouth in "O" shape, shaded lips, French slender kid bebe body with Chevrot-deposed hinged legs, kid-over-metal upper arms, bisque forearms, wooden lower legs. CONDITION: generally excellent. MARKS: Bru Jne 4 (head and shoulderplate). COMMENTS: Bru, circa 1886, the model marketed by Bru as "Bebe Teteur" or Nursing Bru. VALUE POINTS: the bebe has complete rubber ball mechanism in head which, when metal screw at back of head is turned, causes the bebe to "nurse" on bottle; to find the mechanism complete is very rare, and the doll also has her original Bru body and original white pique baby costume and teething ring. $8000/12,000

69. German Bisque Character "Harmus" by Bahr and Proschild

12" (30 cm). Bisque socket head, small brown glass sleep eyes, curly lashes, short feathered brows, accented eye corners, closed mouth with two painted teeth between the accented lips, brunette mohair wig, composition bent limb baby body, well-costumed. CONDITION: generally excellent. MARKS: B.P. (crossed swords) Harmus Germany 630-3. COMMENTS: Bahr and Proschild, circa 1915. VALUE POINTS: superb detail of sculpting and character expression, fine quality bisque and painting on the rare character, original body finish. $800/1100

70. German Bisque Character "Hilda" by Kestner

11" (28 cm). Solid domed bisque socket head, blonde painted baby hair with detail of curls at forehead, blue glass sleep eyes, dark eyeliner encircles the eyecut, feathered brows, accented nostrils and eye corners, open mouth, pale outlined lips with defined tongue tip, two porcelain upper teeth, composition bent limb baby body, antique costume. CONDITION: generally excellent. MARKS: Hilda c. JDK Jr. 1914 ges. gesch N1070 made in Germany 7. COMMENTS: Kestner, circa 1914. VALUE POINTS: very fine detail of modelling and bisque, original body and body finish. $1100/1500

71. French Bisque Bebe Steiner, Figure A, with Rare Bisque Hands

28" (71 cm). Bisque socket head, brown glass paperweight inset eyes with spiral threading, painted lashes with "dot" highlights, rose blushed eyeshadow, thickly fringed brows with feathered highlights and enhancing decorative glaze, accented eye corners, shaded nostrils, pierced ears, blonde mohair wig over Steiner pate, French composition fully jointed body with bisque hands, detailed knuckles, nails and finger blush, lace costume, undergarments, leather shoes, lace and ruffled silk bonnet. CONDITION: generally excellent. MARKS: J. Steiner Bte SGDG Paris Few A 19 (head) Le Petit Parisien Bebe Steiner 1889 (body). COMMENTS: Jules Steiner, circa 1890. VALUE POINTS: beautiful brown-eyed bebe with exquisite detail of complexion blush, luminous brown eyes exactly matching the brows, rare bisque hands. $5000/7500

173. French Bisque Poupee with Deposed Body

15" (38 cm). Bisque swivel head on kid-edged bisque shoulderplate, very wide almond shaped blue enamel inset eyes, painted lashes, arched feathered brows, accented nostrils and eye corners, closed mouth with pale accented lips, pierced ears, blonde mohair wig over cork pate, French stockinette-over-armature body with shapely waist and derriere, bisque hands, bisque lower legs and bare feet. CONDITION: generally excellent. MARKS: 1 (head and shoulderplate). COMMENTS: circa 1868, the doll has the deposed head articulation of Dehors, and the deposed body system of Pannier that was realized by Gesland. VALUE POINTS: very expressive character-like features enhanced by lovely pale bisque, rarer body, beautifully sculpted hands and feet. $2200/2800

172. French Bisque Poupee by Francois Gaultier

15" (38 cm). Bisque swivel head on kid-edged bisque shoulderplate, almond shaped blue glass enamel inset eyes, painted lashes, arched feathered brows, accented nostrils and eye corners, closed mouth with accented lips, pierced ears, brunette mohair wig over cork pate, French kid gusset-jointed body with stitched and separated fingers, costumed elegantly in red silk gown. CONDITION: generally excellent. MARKS: 1 (head and shoulderplate). COMMENTS: attributed to Gaultier, circa 1875. VALUE POINTS: lovely blush on the diminutive fashion lady. $1700/2100

174. French Bisque Poupee with Wooden Articulated Body

15" (38 cm). Bisque swivel head on kid-edged bisque shoulderplate, almond shaped grey glass enamel inset eyes, dark eyeliner encircles the eyecut, painted lashes, arched feathered brows, accented nostrils, closed mouth with accented lips, pierced ears, blonde mohair wig over cork pate, all wooden fully articulated body with shapely torso, dowel-jointing at shoulders, elbows, hips and knees, brown taffeta gown, undergarments, leather boots, bonnet. CONDITION: bisque excellent, body finish structurally excellent albeit original finish is scuffed. MARKS: 1 (head and shoulderplate). COMMENTS: circa 1870. VALUE POINTS: lovely bisque and painting, wooden fully articulated body. $3000/3500

175. French Bisque Poupee with Wooden Articulated Body

17" (43 cm). Bisque swivel head on kid-edged bisque shoulderplate, blue glass enamel inset eyes, dark eyeliner encircles the eyecut, painted lashes, arched feathered brows, accented nostrils, closed mouth with pale outlined lips, unpierced ears, blonde mohair wig over cork pate, French stretched-leather-over-wooden fashion body with shapely waist and derriere, dowel-jointed shoulders, elbows, hips and knees, kid legs from below the knees, bisque arms from below elbows, separately sculpted fingers. CONDITION: generally excellent. COMMENTS: circa 1867. VALUE POINTS: rare body style on the beautiful early poupee with antique burgundy walking suit, undergarments, fur stole, boots, along with antique presentation box. $3000/3500

176. German Paper Mache Lady Doll

12" (30 cm). Paper mache shoulderhead with black sculpted hair arranged in a row of shaped curls at the crown, with rows of horizontal finger curls framing the face, stippling detail around the face, turquoise eyes, black upper eyeliner, single stroke brows, closed mouth with center accent line, blushed cheeks, slender kid body with tiny waist, wooden limbs, green flat painted shoes, blue dotted Swiss gown and undergarments. CONDITION: original finish, some craze on left cheek and shoulderplate. COMMENTS: Germany, circa 1850. VALUE POINTS: rare coiffure, original painting, original body. $500/700

177. German Bisque Child, 969, by Simon and Halbig

15" (38 cm). Bisque socket head, blue glass inset eyes with spiral threading, painted lashes, incised eyeliner, brushstroked and feathered brows, accented nostrils and eye corners, open mouth, outlined lips, four square cut teeth, pierced ears, blonde mohair wig, Sonneberg composition and wooden fully jointed body with straight wrists, nicely costumed. CONDITION: discoloration spot on forehead, otherwise excellent, original body finish. MARKS: 969 S & H dep. COMMENTS: Simon and Halbig, circa 1888. VALUE POINTS: rare model with wonderfully expressive features, beautiful painting. $1100/1600

178. German All-Bisque Miniature by Simon and Halbig

8" (20 cm). Bisque swivel head on kid-edged bisque torso, brown glass inset eyes, painted lashes, brushstroked and feathered brows, accented nostrils, open mouth, accented lips, row of tiny teeth, blonde human hair, peg-jointed bisque arms and legs, painted above-the-knee blue stockings, black two-strap shoes with black bows, nicely costumed. CONDITION: generally excellent. MARKS: 4 886. COMMENTS: Simon and Halbig, circa 1895. VALUE POINTS: rarity factors include large size, swivel head, and high blue stockings. $500/700

179. French Bisque Bebe by Pintel and Godchaux

21" (53 cm). Bisque socket head, very large blue glass paperweight inset eyes, dark eyeliner encircles the eyecuts, lushly painted lashes, rose blushed eyeshadow, arched multi-feathered brows, shaded nostrils, closed mouth with modelled tongue tip, shaded and outlined lips, heart-shaped upper lip, pierced ears, blonde mohair wig over cork pate, French composition and wooden fully jointed body, wearing bronze silk dress with lace trim, undergarments, antique black leather shoes. CONDITION: generally excellent, hands repainted. MARKS: B P. 10 G. COMMENTS: Pintel and Godchaux, circa 1890. VALUE POINTS: captivating large blue eyes with luminous depth, very choice bisque and painting. $3000/4000

180. German Bisque Character "Lori" by Swaine & Co.

24" (61 cm). Solid domed bisque socket head, blonde painted baby hair with soft brushstrokes, almond shaped blue glass sleep eyes, curly painted lashes, incised eyeliner with heavily modelled eyelids, multi-feathered brows, accented nostrils and eye corners, closed mouth modelled as though open with shaded and outlined lips, composition bent limb baby body, antique baby dress and bonnet, undergarments. CONDITION: generally excellent, some body retouch. MARKS: D Lori 1 (incised) Ges Gesch Germany (green stamp). COMMENTS: Swaine & Co, circa 1920. VALUE POINTS: very deeply modelled feature of the expressive faced baby, choice bisque and painting. $1200/1500

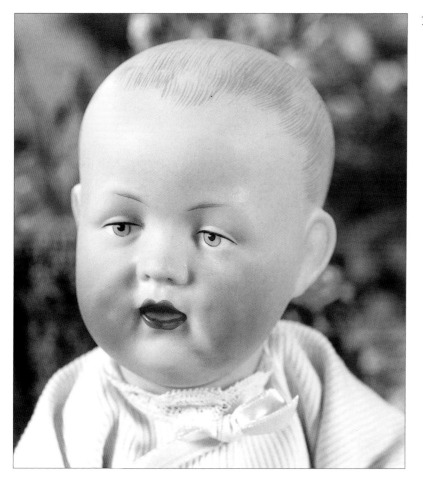

181. German Bisque Character, 2042, by Bruno Schmidt

12" (30 cm). Solid domed bisque socket head, painted blonde baby hair, painted facial features, small blue shaded eyes, heavily modelled eyelids, black upper eyeliner, short feathered brows, accented nostrils, closed mouth modelled as though open, shaded and accented lips, impressed dimples on chin and cheeks, composition bent limb baby body, antique white pique baby suit. CONDITION: generally excellent. MARKS: 2 BSW (in heart) 2042. COMMENTS: Bruno Schmidt, circa 1912. VALUE POINTS: rarer model with superior quality of modelling and bisque, artful painting, original body and body finish. $900/1400

182. German Bisque Googly, 323, by Marseille

9" (23 cm). Bisque socket head, brown glass sleep and side-glancing googly eyes, painted lashes, dash brows, button nose, closed mouth with impish smile, accent line between the lips, brunette mohair wig, composition bent limb baby body, muslin baby suit. CONDITION: generally excellent. MARKS: Germany 323 A 3/0 M. COMMENTS: Marseille, circa 1920. VALUE POINTS: exceptionaly fine quality of bisque on the wide-eyed googly, original body and body finish. $600/900

183. German Bisque Character, 201, by Catterfelder Puppenfabrick

10" (25 cm). Solid domed bisque socket head, blonde painted baby hair, painted facial features, pale blue eyes with grey outline, incised and black upper eyeliner, one stroke brows, closed mouth modelled as though open, shaded and outlined lips, impressed dimples at cheeks and chin, composition and wooden ball-jointed toddler body with side-hip jointing, muslin romper suit. CONDITION: generally excellent. MARKS: C.P. 201 28. COMMENTS: Catterfelder Puppenfabrick, circa 1912, note the close resemblance to #181. VALUE POINTS: rare little character with outstanding quality of modelling and bisque, rarer toddler body. $800/1200

184. Very Rare French Bisque Bebe Steiner, Probably Series G Model

18" (46 cm). Bisque socket head with rounded facial modelling and very full cheeks, blue glass paperweight inset eyes, black painted lashes with "dot" highlights, rose blushed eyeshadow, thickly fringed brows, finely shaped nose with little point, accented nostrils and eye corners, closed mouth with defined space between the outlined shaded lips, impressed vertical groove at center of bottom lip, defined philtrum, pierced ears, blonde mohair wig over Steiner pate, French composition fully jointed body. CONDITION: generally excellent. MARKS: 90 (head) Le Petit ParisienBebe Steiner Medaille d'Or 1889. COMMENTS: Jules Steiner, circa 1889, the doll is a duplicate model to the bebes of that firm signed Series G. VALUE POINTS: very rare bebe of extraordinary beauty and state of preservation, original body, body finish, stunning bisque and painting, antique costume appears original.
$8000/12,000

185. French Bisque Portrait Bebe, 10X, by Jumeau

22" (56 cm). Pressed bisque socket head, large blue glass paperweight inset eyes, painted lashes, dark eyeliner encircles the eyecut, mauve blushed eyeshadow, brushstroked arched brows with multi-feathering, accented eye corners, shaded nostrils, closed mouth with defined space between the shaded and outlined lips, separately applied pierced ears, blonde mohair wig over cork pate, French composition and wooden eight-loose-ball-jointed body with straight wrists. CONDITION: generally excellent. MARKS: 10x (incised on head, with artist checkmarks) Jumeau Medaille d'Or Paris (body). COMMENTS: Emile Jumeau, circa 1884. VALUE POINTS: exceptional beauty of the portrait bebe with exemplary bisque and painting, original body, body finish, antique silk twill gown and matching cape appear original, antique undergarments, straw bonnet, leather boots.
$10,000/13,000

186. An All Original French Bisque Bebe Jumeau
25" (63 cm). Bisque socket head, blue glass
paperweight inset eyes, dark eyeliner
encircles the eyecut, painted lashes,
brushstroked and multi-feathered brows,
shaded nostrils, open mouth, shaded and
accented lips, row of porcelain teeth, pierced
ears, blonde mohair wig over cork pate,
French composition and wooden fully jointed
body. CONDITION: generally excellent.
MARKS: 1907 11 (incised) Tete Jumeau (red
stamp) Bebe Jumeau Diplome d'Honneur
(body label). COMMENTS: Jumeau/SFBJ, circa
1907. VALUE POINTS: very pretty bebe with
nicely blushed complexion, original body and
body finish, original Jumeau muslin chemise
with "Bebe Jumeau" silk banner, original
Jumeau stockings, leather shoes signed "Paris
Bebe 11" and earrings. $3000/3500

187. Petite French Bisque Bebe by Jumeau

12" (30 cm). Bisque socket head, brown glass paperweight inset eyes, lushly painted lashes, widely brushstroked brows, accented nostrils, closed mouth with accented lips, blonde mohair wig over cork pate, pierced ears, French composition and wooden fully jointed body. CONDITION: generally excellent. MARKS: M 2. COMMENTS: Emile Jumeau, the model was commissioned from the firm by an unknown shop, circa 1890. VALUE POINTS: the rare little bebe is enhanced by compelling decoration on the fine creamy bisque, original body and body finish, antique muslin chemise. $2800/3500

188. French Bisque Bebe Phonographe by Jumeau

24" (61 cm). Bisque socket head, blue glass paperweight inset eyes, painted lashes, smoky eyeshadow, brushstroked and multi-feathered brows, shaded nostrils, open mouth, shaded and accented lips, row of porcelain teeth, pierced ears, blonde mohair wig over cork pate, French composition and wooden fully-jointed body with square cut in torso for insertion of mechanical phonograph and cylinders. The phonograph winds from key at back of torso. CONDITION: generally excellent, phonograph needs adjustment but is not overwound, slight body touch-up. MARKS: 11 (and artist checkmarks on head) Bebe Jumeau Bte SGDG Depose (body). COMMENTS: Emile Jumeau, his Bebe Phonographe, based upon the invention of Henri Lioret, was introduced in 1892 and went through several versions; this was the first version. VALUE POINTS: the mechanical doll has lovely bisque face, complete internal parts including numbered phonograph 3883 (3683?) by Lioret and cylinder recording of "Cadet Roussel". $4000/5000

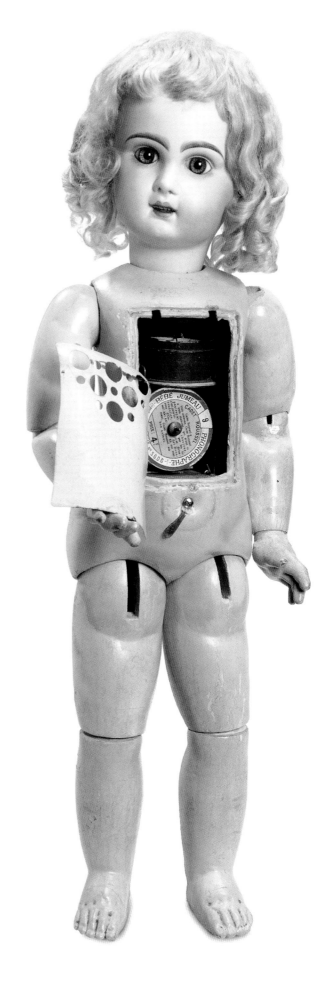

COMMENTS: Bru, circa 1887. VALUE POINTS: very pretty wide-eyed Bru bebe has excellent bisque, original body and body finish, perfect hands, antique dress which may be original, straw bonnet, undergarments, leather shoes with decorative buckles signed "Bru Jne Paris 4". The doll was featured in *Fabulous French Bebe* by Mildred Seeley. $9000/13,000

190. Petite French All Bisque Mignonette

4 1/2" (11 cm). Solid domed bisque swivel head on kid-edged bisque torso, cobalt blue glass enamel inset eyes, painted lashes and brows, accented nostrils, closed mouth with pertly shaped lips, blonde mohair wig, peg-jointed bisque arms and legs, bare feet, original silk and lace dress with straw bonnet, kid slippers. CONDITION: generally excellent. COMMENTS: French, circa 1890. VALUE POINTS: beautiful tiny mignonette with artistic painting of facial features, original costume, bare feet. $900/1200

191. French Bisque Bebe by Denamur

14" (35 cm). Bisque socket head, grey glass enamel inset eyes with rich spiral threading, dark eyeliner encircles the eyecut, long painted lashes, widely feathered brows, accented nostrils and eye corners, closed mouth with accented lips, pierced ears, brunette mohair wig, French composition and wooden fully jointed body, antique maroon silk and lace costume, antique matching set of undergarments maroon stockings and bonnet, leather shoes. CONDITION: generally excellent. MARKS: E. 4 D. COMMENTS: Etienne Denamur, circa 1890. VALUE POINTS: an unusually pretty bebe by this firm with closed mouth, shy expression, original body and body finish. $2200/2800

192. French Bisque Bebe Jumeau, Size 9

20" (51 cm). Bisque socket head, large blue glass paperweight inset eyes, lushly painted lashes, brushstroked and multi-feathered brows, accented eye corners, shaded nostrils, closed mouth with shaded and accented lips, upturned lip corners, pierced ears, blonde mohair wig over cork pate, French composition and wooden fully jointed body, nicely costumed in antique fabrics of maroon silk twill and velvet with fringed trim and decorative buttons, undergarments, leather shoes signed "Paris Bebe". CONDITION: generally excellent. MARKS: Depose Tete Jumeau Bte SGDG 9 (head, and artist checkmarks) Jumeau Medaille d'Or Paris (body). COMMENTS: Emile Jumeau, circa 1890. VALUE POINTS: very pretty classic bebe by Jumeau with dramatic painting of features including rose blushed eyeshadow, original body and body finish. $3500/4500

189. French Bisque Bebe Bru with Original Signed Bru Shoes

16" (40 cm). Bisque swivel head on kid-edged bisque shoulderplate with modelled bosom and shoulderblades, large brown glass paperweight inset eyes, dark eyeliner encircles the eyecut, painted lashes, brushstroked brows, accented eye corners, shaded nostrils, closed mouth with shaded and accented lips, dimpled chin, pierced ears, blonde mohair wig over cork pate, French kid bebe body with slender torso, Chevrot hinged hips, wooden lower legs, kid over metal upper arms, bisque forearms, separately sculpted fingers. CONDITION: generally excellent. MARKS: Bru Jne 4 (head and shoulderplate) (original Bru paper label on torso).

193. German Bisque Child, 146, by Kestner with Excelsior Body

28" (71 cm). Bisque socket head, brown glass sleep eyes, painted lashes, dark eyeliner encircles the eyecut, incised eyeliner, thick brushstroked and feathered brows, accented nostrils and eye corners, open mouth, shaded and outlined lips, four porcelain teeth, blonde mohair wig over plaster pate, dimpled chin, composition and wooden ball-jointed body, antique costume comprising white embroidered dress, undergarments, leather shoes with buckled trim. CONDITION: generally excellent. MARKS: L 1/2 made in Germany 15 1/2 146 (head) Excelsior (body). COMMENTS: Kestner, circa 1910. VALUE POINTS: beautiful sculpting and painting on the large child doll, with original signed body, original body finish. $800/1000

194. German All Bisque Miniature Doll

6" (15 cm). One piece bisque head and torso with very plump facial modelling, brown glass sleep eyes, painted lashes, feathered brows, accented nostrils, closed mouth, accent line between the lips, peg-jointed bisque arms and legs with cupped hands, very plump legs with tiny ankles, white ribbed knee stockings with blue rims, black two strap heeled boots, silk dress and bonnet. CONDITION: 1 (head and under arms). COMMENTS: circa 1890, probably Alt, Beck and Gottschalk. VALUE POINTS: very appealing robust child with artful painting of features. $400/500

195. German Bisque Portrait "Gibson Girl" by Kestner

15" (38 cm). Bisque shoulder head portraying adult woman with slender oval face tilted upward and elongated throat with defined hollow, blue glass sleep eyes, painted lashes and brows, accented nostrils and eye corners, closed mouth with center accent line, blonde mohair wig over plaster pate, slender kid pin-jointed body with sewn darts to suggest female

shaping, bisque forearms with elegantly posed fingers. CONDITION: generally excellent. MARKS: 172 (head) (Kestner crown and streamer label on body). COMMENTS: Kestner's "Gibson Girl" based on the drawings of American illustrator Charles Dana Gibson, circa 1900. VALUE POINTS: rare medium size of the artist-modelled doll, aptly portraying Edwardian society lady, has choicest bisque, original body in very sturdy condition, wig, pate, antique costume may be original. $1100/1500

196. Larger German Bisque Portrait "Gibson Girl" by Kestner

20" (51 cm). Bisque shoulderhead with slender oval face tilted regally upward, elongated throat and defined throat hollow, blue glass sleep eyes with heavily modelled eyelids, mohair lashes, painted lower lashes, accented nostrils and eye corners, aquiline nose, closed mouth with accent line between the lips, blonde mohair wig in upswept fashion over plaster pate, slender kid body with dart-shaped torso, pin-jointed legs, bisque forearms. CONDITION: generally excellent. COMMENTS: Kestner's 172 Gibson Girl model, designed upon the drawings of Charles Dana Gibson, circa 1900. VALUE POINTS: historically important doll, designed by named artist, aptly captures the spirit of the artist's work, with body unique to this doll, original wig, pate, Edwardian style costume. $3000/4000

199. French Red Woolen Fashion Gown and Accessories

To fit fashion doll about 17" (43 cm). Of very lightweight cashmere flannel red wool the gown is decorated with bands of black and ivory soutache embroidery with extra detail at the back; along with a matching red cashmere/ flannel hooded capelet with matching trim, and a white pique flared jacket with wide collar lapels and red soutache trim. Very good condition. Circa 1868. $400/500

200. German All Bisque
Character Designed by Jeanne Orsini

5" (13 cm). One piece bisque head and torso depicting a young girl with very expressive features, elongated throat, tiny squinting blue glass enamel inset eyes, painted lashes, single stroke brows, accented eye corners and nostrils, closed mouth modelled as though open with two rows of teeth, loop-jointed bisque arms and legs, pointing finger on right hands, high white stockings, black one-strap shoes. CONDITION: generally excellent. Marks: J.I.O c. 1920 44 (torso) 47 (inside arms and legs). COMMENTS: designed by American artist Jeanne Orsini, produced in Germany, circa 1920. VALUE POINTS: rare little miniature with distinctive features and fine quality of bisque. $600/800

201. French Bisque Bebe Jumeau, Size 5, with Original Shoes

15" (38 cm). Bisque socket head, blue glass paperweight inset eyes, dark eyeliner encircles the eyecut, lushly painted lashes, brushstroked and multi-feathered brows, accented eye corners, shaded nostrils, closed mouth with shaded and accented lips, pierced ears, blonde mohair wig over cork pate, French composition and wooden fully jointed body with straight wrists, nicely costumed in French style dress. CONDITION: generally excellent. MARKS: Depose Tete Jumeau 5 (head, and artist checkmarks). Jumeau Medaille d'Or Paris (body). COMMENTS: Emile Jumeau, circa 1888. VALUE POINTS: very beautiful bebe has finest creamy bisque, original body and body finish, antique undergarments and bonnet, shoes signed "Paris Depose 5". $3300/3900

202. French Bisque Bebe by Rabery and Delphieu

24" (61 cm). Bisque socket head, large brown glass paperweight inset eyes with spiral threading, dark eyeliner encircles the eyecut, painted lashes, brushstroked and multi-feathered brows, rose blushed eyeshadow, shaded nostrils, closed mouth with shaded and accented lips, defined space between the lips, upturned lip corners, dimpled chin, pierced ears, blonde human hair over cork pate, French composition and wooden fully jointed body with straight wrists, nicely costumed. CONDITION: generally excellent. MARKS: R. 3 D. COMMENTS: Rabery and Delphieu, circa 1888. VALUE POINTS: deeply sculpted features enhanced by fine cameo-like complexion, beautiful painting of features, original body and body finish, antique undergarments and leather shoes. $3300/4100

203. German Bisque Character, 116/A, by Kammer and Reinhardt

16" (40 cm). Bisque socket head, brown glass sleep eyes, painted dark curly lashes, short feathered brows, accented nostrils, closed mouth modelled as though open with smiling expression, two beaded upper teeth, shaded and accented lips, brunette human hair, composition bent limb baby body. CONDITION: generally excellent. MARKS: K*R Simon & Halbig 116/A 42. COMMENTS: Kammer and Reinhardt, circa 1912. VALUE POINTS: very fine detail of sculpting featuring laughter crinkles, dimples at cheeks and eye corners, choice bisque, original body and body finish, antique costume. $2200/2800

204. Three German All Bisque Kewpies

5"-7" (13-18 cm). Each is one piece bisque figure of standing Kewpie with loop-jointed arms, blonde painted topknot and side-curls, side-glancing eyes, blue wings, starfish-modelled hands. The two smaller Kewpies have opposite glancing eyes so appear to be gazing at each other. CONDITION: generally excellent. MARKS: O'Neill (feet) (and two with original paper labels). COMMENTS: designed by Rose O'Neill, produced in Germany, circa 1915. VALUE POINTS: appealing trio with variations in painting. $300/400

205. French Bisque Kiss-Throwing Bru Bebe

11" (28 cm). Bisque socket head, small brown glass enamel inset eyes, painted lashes, fringed brows, accented nostrils and eye corners, closed mouth with accented lips, pierced ears, blonde mohair wig over cork pate, French composition body with one piece left arm and legs, right arm is jointed at elbow and connected to torso pull-string; when string is pulled the doll brings her hand up to her mouth as though throwing kisses. CONDITION: generally excellent. MARKS: Bru Jne R 2. COMMENTS: Bru, circa 1895. VALUE POINTS: petite size of the late bebe from the illustrious firm has deposed kissing action that functions well. $3000/4000

206. French All Bisque Miniature

5" (13 cm). One piece bisque head and torso, cobalt blue glass enamel inset eyes, closed mouth, brunette mohair bobbed wig, peg-jointed bisque arms and legs, hands cupped, painted white stockings and fancy yellow boots antique costume. CONDITION: re-glue on left upper arm and right upper leg. MARKS: 3/0. COMMENTS: circa 1890. VALUE POINTS: appealing little closed mouth all-bisque. $200/250

207. French Bisque Toddler, 247, by SFBJ

27" (68 cm). Bisque socket head, brown glass inset eyes, mohair lashes, painted lower lashes, short feathered brows, accented nostrils, closed mouth modelled as though open with shaded lips and two beaded upper teeth, blonde human hair in bobbed style, composition and wooden fully-jointed toddler body with side-hip jointing, nicely made sailor costume. CONDITION: generally excellent. MARKS: 23 France SFBJ 247 Paris 12. COMMENTS: SFBJ, circa 1918. VALUE POINTS: the rosy complexioned toddler has original body and body finish, antique mariner cap, appealing expression. $900/1200

208. French Bisque Bebe Steiner, Figure A

23" (58 cm). Bisque socket head, blue glass paperweight inset eyes, painted lashes with "dot" highlights, fringed brows, shaded nostrils, closed mouth with shaded and outlined lips, pierced ears, brunette mohair wig over Steiner pate, French composition and wooden fully jointed body. CONDITION: generally excellent. MARKS: Steiner Paris Fre A 15 (head) Le Petit Parisien Bebe Steiner (body). COMMENTS: Jules Steiner, circa 1890. VALUE POINTS: very beautiful bisque and painting on the shy-faced bebe, with original signed body, original body finish, turquoise silk dress, antique undergarments, boots and cap. $4000/5000

209. French Bisque "Gigoteur" by Jules Steiner

18" (46 cm). Solid domed head with flat-cut neck socket, large blue glass inset eyes, painted lashes, fringed brows, rose blushed eyeshadow, accented eye corners, shaded nostrils, open mouth with shaded lips, two rows of tiny porcelain teeth, brunette mohair wig, carton torso containing clockwork mechanism, composition arms, wire-hinged legs, paper mache lower legs, when key wound the bebe turns head from side to side, cries mama and waves arms and legs in the air. CONDITION: generally excellent. MARKS: Le Petit Parisien Bebe Steiner Medaille d'Or Paris 1889. COMMENTS: the model was marketed as "gigoteur" by the Steiner firm and was one of their longest lasting models, circa 1885. VALUE POINTS: pretty example of the crying bebe wears original costume typical of Paris doll shop Au Nain Bleu, has lovely bisque and painting, functions well. $2200/2800

210. Petite French Bisque Bebe by Steiner with Brown Eyes

8" (20 cm). Bisque socket head, brown glass inset eyes, painted lashes, thickly fringed brows, accented nostrils and eye corners, closed mouth with shaded and outlined lips, pierced ears, brunette mohair wig over Steiner pate, French composition body jointed at shoulders and hips. CONDITION: generally excellent. MARKS: A o Paris (head) Le Petit Parisien Bebe Steiner (torso). COMMENTS: Jules Steiner, circa 1890. VALUE POINTS: beautiful painting on the petite bebe with original body and body finish, original muslin chemise, wig, bonnet, shoes and socks. $2500/3000

211. German All Bisque Miniature in Original Costume

6" (15 cm). One piece bisque head and torso, brown glass inset eyes, painted lashes, brushstroked brows, accented nostrils and eye corners, closed mouth with accented lips, blonde mohair wig, peg-jointed arms and legs, painted white stockings and black two strap heeled shoes. CONDITION: generally excellent. MARKS: 61-8 (head and arms). COMMENTS: circa 1890. VALUE POINTS: the closed mouth doll wears his original knit swimsuit and cap. $500/600

212. Petite French Bisque Bebe by Steiner with Blue Eyes

8" (20 cm). Bisque socket head, large blue glass inset eyes, painted lashes, brushstroked and multi-feathered brows, accented nostrils and eye corners, closed mouth with accent line between the lips, pierced ears, blonde mohair wig, French composition body jointed at shoulders and hips. CONDITION: generally excellent. MARKS: Le Parisien (red stamp on head) A-o Paris (incised on head) Bebe Le Parisien Medaille d'Or Paris (body). COMMENTS: Jules Steiner, circa 1890. VALUE POINTS: very beautiful tiny doll has her original body and body finish, superb antique costume. $2500/3000

213. German Brown-Complexioned Bisque Doll, 949, by Simon and Halbig

19" (48 cm). Bisque socket head with light brown complexion, brown glass inset eyes, painted black lashes, incised eyeliner, black brushstroked and feathered brows, accented nostrils and eye corners, open mouth with very slightly parted lips, row of tiny porcelain teeth, pierced ears, black fleecy wig, brown composition and wooden fully jointed body. CONDITION: generally excellent, flakes at pierced ear holes. MARKS: S 12 H 949. COMMENTS: Simon and Halbig, circa 1890. VALUE POINTS: very unusual pale brown complexion is enhanced by deep sculpting of long-faced features, lovely antique costume. $1100/1600

214. French Brown-Complexioned Bisque Bebe by Jules Steiner

15" (38 cm). Bisque socket head with amber brown complexion, brown glass paperweight inset eyes, dark painted lashes, dark brown fringed brows, accented nostrils, closed mouth with outlined lips, pierced ears, black fleecy wig, French composition fully jointed body, antique costume including mauve pinafore with child-embroidered cat on center pocket. CONDITION: generally excellent. MARKS: J. Steiner Bte SGDG Paris Fre A 7 (head) Le Petit Parisien Bebe J. Steiner Medaille d'Or Paris 1889 (body). COMMENTS: Jules Steiner, circa 1890. VALUE POINTS: beautiful lustrous patina on the amber brown complexion is most appealing, original body and body finish. $3000/4000

215. Rare German Bisque Character, 1368, by Simon and Halbig
14" (35 cm). Bisque socket head with ebony black complexion, brown glass inset eyes, incised upper eyeliner, single stroke black brows, accented eye corners and nostrils, open mouth with coral painted lips, four porcelain teeth, pierced ears, black fleecy wig, black composition and wooden ball-jointed body, antique costume. CONDITION: generally excellent. MARKS: 1368 Germany Simon & Halbig S&H 4. COMMENTS: Simon and Halbig, from their exotic character series, circa 1910. VALUE POINTS: rare character model whose rich ebony black complexion is enhanced by choice sculpting. $4000/5000

216. French Bisque Premiere Bebe Jumeau

16" (40 cm). Pressed bisque socket head, large blue glass enamel inset eyes with spiral threading, dark eyeliner encircles the eyecut, painted lashes with feathered highlights, mauve blushed eyeshadow, accented nostrils, closed mouth with pale outlined lips, pierced ears, auburn mohair wig over cork pate, French composition and wooden eight-loose-ball-jointed body with straight wrists. CONDITION: generally excellent. MARKS: 7 (head) Jumeau Medaille d'Or Paris (body). COMMENTS: Emile Jumeau, circa 1878, his early model bebe. VALUE POINTS: beautiful model of early bebe has appealing shy expression, excellent bisque and painting, original body and body finish, antique teal blue costume, undergarments, bonnet, black leather Jumeau shoes signed "Paris Depose". $5500/7500

217. Beautiful Large French Bisque Portrait Bebe, Size 10, by Jumeau

22" (56 cm). Pressed bisque socket head with very full cheeks, blue glass enamel eyes in hand-cut eye socket, dark eyeliner encircles the eyecuts, painted lashes, brushstroked and feathered brows, accented eye corners, shaded nostrils, closed mouth with upturned lip corners, outlined lips, separately modelled pierced ears, original blonde mohair wig over cork pate, French composition and wooden eight-loose-ball-jointed body with plump limbs, straight wrists. CONDITION: generally excellent. MARKS: 10 (and artist checkmarks on head) Jumeau Medaille d'Or Paris (body) (Gesland doll shop label on torso). COMMENTS: Emile Jumeau, circa 1880. VALUE POINTS: an early model bebe with superb detail of modelling and painting, transfixing expression, original body and body finish, antique costume comprising blue velvet coat, silk lined bonnet, winter wool dress, black stockings, undergarments, black leather shoes. $8000/11,000

218. French Bisque Multi-Faced Character Doll by Jumeau

18" (46 cm). Bisque socket head has two different faces which are alternately revealed by turning the brass knob at top of head; one face portrays a crying child with brown glass inset eyes, painted lashes, brushstroked brows, accented nostrils of funny pushed-up nose, closed mouth modelled as though open and crying, modelled tongue and row of teeth; the other face portrays a laughing child with brown glass inset eyes, painted lashes, brushstroked brows, shaded nostrils, closed mouth modelled as though open with a wide-beaming smile, modelled tongue tip and teeth, shaded and accented lips. The head is enclosed within a cardboard hood which attaches to the doll's torso, and which is covered by brown mohair wig and lace bonnet; the body has composition and wooden fully jointed limbs with unusual pull-string crier that cries "mama" and also a bird cry. CONDITION: generally excellent. COMMENTS: Emile Jumeau, circa 1898, the double-faced model incorporates his 211 and 203 character series. VALUE POINTS: the rare model has wonderfully modelled features, is well preserved including teardrop, unusual crier, and original Jumeau chemise dress.
$8000/11,000

**219. Rare French Bisque Crying Doll,
211, from Jumeau Character Series**

24" (61 cm). Bisque socket head, very
narrow squinting brown glass enamel
inset eyes, painted lashes, brushstroked
brows, accented nostrils, closed mouth
modelled as though open and crying, with
modelled tongue, shaded and outlined
lips, row of modelled teeth, separately
modelled pierced ears, auburn mohair
wig, French composition and wooden
fully jointed body. CONDITION: left half of
forehead has been broken (one piece) and
neatly reglued, another hairline on right
forehead, incomplete restoration on lower
left eye rim, body finish worn and
retouched. MARKS: 211 Depose Tete
Jumeau Bte SGDG 10 (head) Bebe
Jumeau Diplome d'Honneur (body).
COMMENTS: Emile Jumeau, circa 1892.
VALUE POINTS: very rare character retains
original painting of features, deeply
sculpted modelling, antique mariner suit.
$8000/12,000

220. French Bisque Bebe by Juillien

19" (48 cm). Bisque socket head with long-faced modelling, amber brown glass paperweight inset eyes, dark eyeliner encircles the eyecut, painted lashes, brushstroked and feathered brows, mauve blushed eyeshadow, accented eye corners and nostrils, closed mouth, shaded and accented lips, pierced ears, brunette mohair wig, French composition and wooden fully jointed body, silk dress. CONDITION: generally excellent, some light body touch-up. MARKS: Juillien 7. COMMENTS: Juillien, circa 1890. VALUE POINTS: very pretty amber eyes and appealing wistful expression. $2500/3500

221. Petite French Bisque Bebe by Juillien, Size 1

11" (28 cm). Bisque socket head, blue glass paperweight inset eyes, painted lashes, rose blushed eyeshadow, brushstroked and feathered brows, accented nostrils and eye corners, closed mouth with accented lips, pierced ears, brunette human hair over cork pate, French composition and wooden fully jointed body. CONDITION: generally excellent. MARKS: Juillien 1 (head) Bebe Incassable L'Universelle (paper seal on back). COMMENTS: Juillien, circa 1890. VALUE POINTS: well-preserved petite bebe has fine bisque and decoration, original wig, muslin chemise, body label; the doll was featured in several books by Mildred Seeley including *Millettes*. $2200/2800

222. French Bisque Bebe Jumeau, Size 9

22" (56 cm). Bisque socket head, brown glass paperweight inset eyes, lushly painted lashes, incised eyeliner, brushstroked and feathered brows, shaded nostrils, closed mouth with richly shaded lips, pierced ears, blonde human hair over cork pate, French composition and wooden fully jointed body, nicely costumed in blue silk twill, undergarments, leather shoes, bonnet. CONDITION: generally excellent, hands repainted. MARKS: Depose Tete Jumeau Bte SGDG 9 (and artist checkmarks). COMMENTS: Emile Jumeau, circa 1890. VALUE POINTS: fine lustrous patina to the well painted features, luminous brown eyes. $3300/3800

223. French Bisque Bebe Jumeau "Dep", Size 10

23" (58 cm). Bisque socket head, brown glass paperweight inset eyes, painted lower lashes with "dot" highlights, brushstroked brows with decorative glaze, accented eye corners, open mouth, shaded and outlined lips, four teeth, pierced ears, blonde ringlet curls, French composition and wooden fully jointed body. CONDITION: bisque excellent, body finish is original but flaking. MARKS: Dep Tete Jumeau 10 (head) Bebe Jumeau Diplome d'Honneur (body). COMMENTS: SFBH, circa 1910. VALUE POINTS: with bright-eyed child wears her original French silk dress, bonnet and blue silk shoes signed "Paris Depose 10". $1100/1500

224. German Bisque Character, 251, for George Borgfeldt
12" (30 cm). Bisque socket head, small blue glass inset eyes, painted lashes, short feathered brows, accented nostrils, closed mouth in fretful expression with strong accent line on upper lip, tiny tongue tip between the lips, brunette human hair, composition and wooden ball-jointed body, nicely costumed. CONDITION: generally excellent. MARKS: 251 G.B. Germany A 410 M. DRGM. COMMENTS: Armand Marseille for Borgfeldt, circa 1920. VALUE POINTS: very expressive features on the little pouty faced child. $600/800

225. German Bisque Character, 1488, by Simon and Halbig
9" (23 cm). Bisque socket head, blue glass sleep eyes, painted lashes, short feathered brows, accented nostrils, closed mouth with expressively shaped lips, blonde mohair wig, composition bent limb baby body, antique costume. CONDITION: generally excellent. MARKS: 1488 Simon & Halbig 3. COMMENTS: Simon and Halbig, circa 1915. VALUE POINTS: rare little character in unusually petite size is most appealing, original body and body finish. $900/1200

226. German Bisque Character, 115/A, by Kammer and Reinhardt
11" (28 cm). Bisque socket head, blue glass sleep eyes, dark eyeliner encircles the eyecut, painted lashes, short feathered brows, accented nostrils, closed mouth with pouty expression, accent line between the lips, blonde mohair wig, composition bent limb baby body, antique baby costume. CONDITION: generally excellent. MARKS: K*R Simon & Halbig 115/A 34. COMMENTS: Kammer and Reinhardt, circa 1912, their model marketed as "Phillip". VALUE POINTS: gentle-faced character with wistful expression has very choice bisque and painting, original body and body finish. $1800/2500

227. German Bisque Character, 6969, with Glass Eyes by Gebruder Heubach
10" (25 cm). Pink tinted bisque socket head, small dark blue glass sleep eyes, painted lashes, incised eyeliner, feathered brows, accented nostrils and eye corners, closed mouth with full lips in pouty expression enhanced by accent lines, brunette human hair braids, composition bent limb baby body, antique baby dress and sweater, undergarments, shoes. CONDITION: generally excellent. MARKS: 6969 Germany 2. COMMENTS: Gebruder Heubach, circa 1915. VALUE POINTS: rare little model has very choice bisque and painting. $1100/1400

228. German Bisque Child, 192, by Kammer and Reinhardt from Matthes Toy Shop of Berlin

14" (35 cm). Bisque socket head, small blue glass sleep eyes, painted curly lashes, brushstroked and feathered brows, accented eye corners and nostrils, open mouth with outlined lips, two small porcelain teeth, pierced ears, blonde mohair wig, early composition and wooden ball-jointed body with elongated torso, pull-string mama crier, antique ivory silk dress, undergarments, shoes, stockings. CONDITION: generally excellent. MARKS: 192 (head) Ed. Matthes Berlin Leipzigstr.115-116 (body label). COMMENTS: Kammer and Reinhardt, circa 1892, the doll was offered by the famous Berlin doll shop of Matthes. VALUE POINTS: rarer model with beautiful expression, unusual signed body with original finish, antique costume. $800/1000

229. German Bisque Closed Mouth Child by Kestner

12" (30 cm). Bisque socket head with rounded facial modelling, plump cheeks, small blue glass sleep eyes, painted lashes, arched feathered brows, accented nostrils and eye corners, closed mouth with outlined lips, blonde mohair wig over plaster pate, early composition and wooden fully jointed body with straight wrists, antique costume. CONDITION: generally excellent. COMMENTS: Kestner, circa 1890. VALUE POINTS: pretty child with pouty expression enhanced by deepest modelling of philtrum and accents around the mouth, choice bisque, original body and body finish. $1200/1800

230. French Bisque Bebe, Size 1, by Francois Gaultier

10" (25 cm). Bisque socket head, large blue glass paperweight inset eyes with spiral threading, dark eyeliner encircles the eyecuts, arched feathered brows, accented nostrils and eye corners, closed mouth with accented lips, pierced ears, blonde mohair wig over cork pate, French composition and wooden fully jointed body, nicely costumed in antique dress, undergarments, slippers, bonnet. CONDITION: generally excellent, right pierced earhole pulled through. MARKS: F. 1 G. (block letters). COMMENTS: Francois Gaultier, circa 1882. VALUE POINTS: rare and appealing size 1 of the early block letter bebe has well modelled features, original body and body finish. $3000/3500

231. Sonneberg Bisque
Closed Mouth Mystery Doll

13" (33 cm). Bisque socket head with flattened solid dome and long-faced modelling, blue glass enamel inset eyes, painted lashes, brushstroked brows, accented nostrils and eye corners, closed mouth with accent line between the lips, pierced ears, blonde mohair wig, Sonneberg composition and wooden fully jointed body with straight wrists, well costumed in green wool coat with black velvet and lambswool trim, matching muff and cap, old leather shoes. CONDITION: generally excellent. MARKS: 4. COMMENTS: mystery maker, circa 1885. VALUE POINTS: very expressive features enhanced by deep sculpting. $900/1200

232. French Bisque Poupee
by Francois Gaultier

24" (61 cm). Bisque swivel head on kid-edged bisque shoulderplate, dark blue glass paperweight inset eyes, dark eyeliner encircles the eyecuts, painted lashes, rose blushed eyeshadow, brushstroked and feathered brows, accented eye corners and nostrils, closed mouth with accented lips, pierced ears, blonde human hair over cork pate, French kid gusset jointed fashion body with bisque arms from below the elbows, nicely shaped fingers with defined knuckles and nails, well costumed in antique green and black taffeta, with black lace and beaded fringe trim, undergarments, boots, bonnet. CONDITION: generally excellent, elbow kid joints a bit weak. MARKS: 7 (head) F.G. 7 (shoulderplate). COMMENTS: Francois Gaultier, circa 1875. VALUE POINTS: regal and elegant large fashion lady with lovely bisque and painting. $2500/3000

233. French Bisque Kid-Bodied Bebe by Gaultier

16" (40 cm). Bisque swivel head on kid-edged bisque shoulderplate, brown enamel glass inset eyes with dark eyeliner, painted curly lashes, rose blushed eyeshadow, brushstroked and feathered brows, accented eye corners and nostrils, closed mouth with shaded and outlined lips, pierced ears, auburn mohair wig over cork pate, French kid gusset jointed bebe body with square cut collarette, bisque forearms with nicely sculpted definition of hands, knuckles and nails, antique costume. CONDITION: generally excellent. MARKS: F. 2/0 G. (head) F.G. (left shoulder) 2/0 (right shoulder). COMMENTS: Francois Gaultier, the earliest model bebe from that firm, circa 1880. VALUE POINTS: the rarity of the early bebe is rivalled by her beauty, choice bisque and painting, rarer body style with perfect bisque hands. $5000/7500

234. German Bisque Portrait of Asian Child, 1199, by Simon and Halbig

12" (30 cm). Bisque socket head with dark amber tinted complexion, brown glass inset eyes in side-slanted cut, painted dark lashes, black feathered brows, accented nostrils and eye corners, closed mouth with accented lips, four porcelain upper teeth, black mohair queue, amber tinted composition and wooden ball-jointed body. CONDITION: generally excellent. MARKS: SH 1199 Dep 3. COMMENTS: Simon and Halbig, circa 1900. VALUE POINTS: exceptional quality of modelling of facial features, lovely bisque, antique costume. $1200/1800

235. German Bisque Portrait of Asian Child, 1329, by Simon and Halbig

12" (30 cm). Bisque socket head with golden-amber tinted complexion, small brown glass sleep eyes, painted lashes, black brushstroked and multi-feathered brows, accented nostrils, open mouth, shaded and accented lips, four porcelain teeth, pierced ears, black mohair wig in upswept fashion, amber tinted composition and wooden ball-jointed body, antique costume. CONDITION: generally excellent. MARKS: 1329 Simon & Halbig Germany S&H. COMMENTS: Simon and Halbig, circa 1900. VALUE POINTS: the golden-amber complexion is most beautiful, enhanced by richly tinted brows and lips, original wig, original body and body finish. $1200/1500

236. Petite Sonneberg Bisque Portrait of Asian Child

10" (25 cm). Bisque socket head with flattened solid dome, brown glass enamel inset eyes, painted lashes, brown side-feathered brows, accented nostrils and eye corners, closed mouth with accent line between the lips, pierced ears, amber tinted Sonneberg composition fully jointed body, Chinese silk costume. CONDITION: generally excellent. MARKS: 220. COMMENTS: attributed to Bahr and Proschild, circa 1885. VALUE POINTS: rare early model in most appealing petite size, beautiful expression. $800/1100

237. French Bisque Bebe Jumeau in Original Jumeau Factory Chemise
28" (71 cm). Bisque socket head, large brown glass paperweight inset eyes, dark eyeliner encircles the eyecut, lushly painted dark lashes, incised eyeliner, widely arched brushstroked brows with multi-feathered detail, shaded nostrils, open mouth, shaded and accented lips, row of porcelain teeth, pierced ears, original brunette human hair hand-tied wig over cork pate, French composition and wooden fully jointed body. CONDITION: generally excellent. MARKS: 13 (head) Tete Jumeau (red stamp on head) Bebe Jumeau Diplome d'Honneur (body label). COMMENTS: SFBJ, circa 1900. VALUE POINTS: outstanding example of Jumeau/SFBJ bebe retains the very choice creamy bisque of the earlier models with richest quality of facial painting, original body and body finish, wig, pate, Jumeau red flowered chemise, stockings and shoes signed "Paris Depose 13" with bee symbol. $3000/4000

238. French Paper Mache Poupee in Folklore Costume
12" (30 cm). Paper mache shoulderhead with solid dome and slender facial modelling, black enamel inset eyes with painted lashes, arched feathered brows, aquiline nose, open mouth with slightly parted lips, row of teeth, brunette human hair wig over black painted skull cap, pink kid fashion body with one piece shapely limbs, tiny waist, mitten hands. CONDITION: generally excellent. COMMENTS: French, circa 1850. VALUE POINTS: the early doll retains fine original ivory-like complexion, very sturdy body, has original wig, and wears original French folklore costume of Haute-Pyrenees. $700/900

Index